How to Repair

MAJOR
APPLIANCES

By

Ernest Tricomi

HOWARD W. SAMS & CO., INC.
THE BOBBS-MERRILL CO., INC.
INDIANAPOLIS · KANSAS CITY · NEW YORK

SECOND EDITION

FOURTH PRINTING—1971

International Standard Book Number: 0-672-20650-1
Library of Congress Catalog Card Number: 68-24770

PREFACE

If any one thing can be said to characterize the modern home, it is the 60-cycle hum of electric motors working quietly in almost every room of the house. One motor pumps refrigerant through a tall insulated cabinet designed to keep food fresh and palatable for days and weeks. Another motor strokes an agitator deep in suds to wash clothes sparkling clean. Still another churns up a miniature hurricane of hot, sudsy water against the dinner dishes, leaving them cleaner, brighter, and more sanitary than grandma ever could with all the hard work and pride at her command.

And it doesn't stop there. Powerful, motor-driven jaws grind up garbage and flush it down the drain; volumes of warm air float through freshly-laundered clothes to leave them just dry enough to iron; and another blower draws hot moist air into a window-mounted cabinet, returning cool, dry air to condition the environment of the room. In the meantime, an electric or gas water heater pours heat energy into gallons of water, on tap to lighten the housewife's daily "drudgery."

Behind it all is the pervasive hum of 60-cycle alternating current, driving the motors and generating the heat that bring alive all the gleaming, useful, and efficient major appliances we will study in this book.

To lead the reader through an exhaustive analysis of every make and model of machine would be virtually impossible, and such a book would become outdated even before it was published. Instead, the theory, functioning, electrical characteristics, and major components of typical appliances are stressed. This approach is possible because each type of major home appliance is similar to all others of the same type in nearly all important respects. Thus, the emphasis here will be on learning the *how* and *why* of an appliance so that the reader equipped with normal intelligence and some degree of mechanical aptitude can answer for himself the *what* and the *where* of detailed repairs and servicing.

Whenever one detail of functioning in a particular make or model differs from that found in others, it has been explained and described as fully as space permits.

No attempt has been made to give step-by-step disassembly, since this is largely a matter of common sense. However, if it becomes necessary to disassemble a component (such as a transmission, compressor, timer, or other assembly) which is normally not repaired in the field, it is recommended that the manufacturer's service literature be consulted for guidance. This is also desirable if it is necessary to replace a major portion of the wiring harness.

ERNEST TRICOMI

CONTENTS

CHAPTER 1

HOME APPLIANCE REPAIRING

Major home appliances need electricity, if not as the major source of energy, at least as a secondary one to provide light for control panels, to drive motors, and to run clocks. Even the automatic gas water heater, with no visible connection to house current, uses a weak, self-generated current flow to hold open a gas solenoid valve. It is important, then, for the servicing technician to have at his command a good understanding of the properties of electricity, as well as its application in the home.

Electricity is available in two distinct types—alternating current and direct current. When direct current is used, it is found in commercial and industrial establishments and has no application in the appliances discussed in this book.

To gain a better understanding of the electrical components in appliances, the serviceman should have a speaking acquaintance with electrical terms. Most introductions to electricity draw a comparison between electricity flowing through a wire and water flowing through a pipe. This discussion will be no exception for this is an excellent way of illustrating the behavior of electricity. Just remember, though, that electricity flows with lightning speed through its "pipes."

ELECTRICAL TERMS AND DEFINITIONS

Voltage is a measure of electromotive force, or pressure, without regard to flow; it can be compared to the pressure of water, whether it is moving or standing, in a pipe. One volt is the amount of electrical force which, when applied to a conductor having a resistance of 1 ohm, will produce a current of 1 ampere. Voltage is measured by a voltmeter.

The current through a conductor is measured in units called amperes (or amps) and is measured with an ammeter. Amperage can be compared to gallons per minute of water flow through a pipe.

Resistance is the opposition a conductor offers to the flow of an electrical current. This opposition in a conductor may be compared to pipes of small and large diameter. The small-diameter pipe restricts the rate of flow (small-diameter wire has a higher resistance). A large-diameter pipe would permit more gallons of water to flow past a given point per minute (large-diameter wire has a lower resistance). The unit of resistance is the ohm, measured with an ohmmeter.

Wattage is the power required to do work. Electrical power is measured in watts and can be related to horsepower measurements of mechanical force, i.e., 1 horsepower is equal to 746 watts. Power is measured with a wattmeter.

Phase is the number of distinctly different voltage waves in a commercial power source; it is usually delivered to users as a single- or three-phase service. Homes, offices, stores, and small industrial plants use single-phase service. Single-phase current alone is unable to start the rotor of an electric motor, therefore, start windings, or start capacitors, must be used in most motors; or a split-phase motor design may be used.

Three-phase service is more expensive, but it has the advantage of permitting motors of simpler and smaller design which can start themselves. Three-phase service also allows smoother operation of motors.

Alternating current (AC) is a flow of current which continuously peaks in one direction, reverses to zero, then peaks in the opposite direction. The direction of flow of alternating current changes rapidly, resulting in surges of electricity from a generator to the user and back to the generator again at varying rates, e.g., 60 cycles per second (cps) or 400 cps. Alternating current is in widespread use in the United States because it is cheaper to generate and deliver than direct current (DC). In parts of Europe, DC is used, necessitating modification of American-made appliances when exported.

Cycles per second is a measure of the *frequency* at which AC changes direction. Most communities in the United States have 60-cycle AC, meaning that the current changes direction 60 times each second. In some communities, electrical supplies are 50-cycle per second.

House Wiring

While house wiring is not properly the prime responsibility of an appliance-service technician, he should be concerned about it to the extent that any installation made will be a safe and efficient one. Good house wiring requires enough circuits in the home for uniform distribution of the load. The circuits must have wires sufficiently large in diameter to carry a full load safely and economically without causing a drop in voltage before the current reaches the appliance. Outlets should be close enough to the appliance to permit the line cord to be plugged directly into them, without the use of extension cords. All electrical codes prohibit splicing exposed line cords, and most of them frown on the use of extension cords—no matter how well they may be installed.

Good house wiring demands a modern, well designed control box equipped with fuses or circuit breakers of the correct rating. Perhaps as important as any other consideration in electrical wiring is neatness and workmanship. A sloppy terminal connection or a loosely soldered electrical component is a source of danger.

Alternating current is provided by the utility company as high voltage. Before it enters the home, it is "stepped down" by a transformer located on a power-line pole. From this transformer it enters the home as either two-wire (115 volts) or three-wire (115 and/or 230 volts) service. Most modern homes are equipped with three-wire service, even though there is no immediate requirement for 230 volts. When a 230-volt appliance, such as an air conditioner or electric clothes dryer, is installed, a branch line must be run from the control center to a special outlet. This outlet, of course, must never be used for any 115-volt device or a burnout will result.

Fusing

Fuses are used to protect the house wiring system and the appliance from short circuits and overloads. Fuses usually consist of a strip of metal which melts at a relatively low temperature. When the fuse is intact, current flows through the metal just as it would through any good conductor. If a sudden surge of current (amperage) occurs, due to a short

9

circuit or an overload, the accelerated rate of flow of electricity through the narrow strip of metal will generate enough heat to melt it, thus interrupting the current.

In some appliances, notably garbage disposers, a momentary overload is normal during the time necessary for the drive motor to gain momentum. In these cases, a thermal-delay fuse (*Fusetron,* etc.) is used. This type of fuse will tolerate an overload for a short period, but it will open instantly if a short circuit develops.

Fuses are of the screw-in or plug type (Fig. 1-1A), or the cartridge type (Fig. 1-1B). Usually plug fuses are used in 115-volt lines, while cartridge fuses may be used in 230-volt, and higher power lines. Both are rated in amperes, indicating the maximum amount of current the metal strip or internal element will carry without melting (blowing). Plug fuses are rated up to 30 amperes, while cartridge fuses may be rated from 3 amperes to as high as 600 amperes.

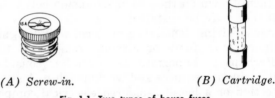

(A) Screw-in.   *(B) Cartridge.*

Fig. 1-1. Two types of house fuses.

Another means of protecting a line is with a circuit breaker, most of which employ an electromagnet which breaks the circuit when its magnetic field is intensified to the maximum allowance. Having broken the circuit, the device is prevented from reclosing by the force of a spring. Thus, circuit breakers must be reset manually, even if the cause of the overload is corrected. If, when the device is reset, the overload condition persists, the circuit breaker will open the circuit immediately.

Grounding

Electricity, like water, follows the path of least resistance. Suppose that the insulation has worn off and a bare wire touches the exterior metal cabinet of an appliance. If the cabinet is properly grounded, the electricity will find an easy path to the ground through the ground wire which is connected to a cold-water pipe. Any lesser conductor of electricity (such as a human body) which may also touch the cabinet at the same time, will have no current flow through it, since it offers more resistance than the ground wire. If no other path to ground exists, however, then the electricity will flow through the body, with sometimes disastrous results.

Those appliances which should be grounded, such as washers, dryers, dishwashers, air conditioners, and ranges, are always accompanied by complete grounding instructions and kits. Do not defeat the purpose of these grounds by finding ways to bypass them—they are installed to protect against fatal shocks and demand very careful installation.

Wire Capacity

As mentioned before, the larger the diameter of a wire, the less resistance it will offer to an electrical current. Wire diameter is given a numerical gauge value; the smaller numbers indicate larger diameters. Table 1-1 lists the capacity of each gauge from 0 to 14 in maximum allowable amperes:

Table 1-1. Maximum Allowable Current-Carrying Capacity of Copper Wire

Wire Gauge	Amperes
14	15
12	20
10	30
8	45
6	65
4	85
3	100
2	115
1	130
0	150

The capacity of the house electrical service is directly related to the load-carrying capacity of the wire used. Every home should have a total capacity of at least 100 amperes, with one or two appliance branch circuits of 20-ampere capacity. Consult Table 1-1 and notice that a 20-ampere circuit should have No. 12 wire.

SAFETY PRECAUTIONS

The first rule when working with electricity is to disconnect the appliance from the outlet, or remove the fuse from the circuit. Even this rule is not completely foolproof, however, because the wrong fuse or the wrong wall plug might be removed. Therefore, after disconnecting the circuit, test the line with a continuity tester to make sure that no voltage is present.

Personal safety is a vital consideration, of course, but the safety of the user is of equal concern. Connections should be secure so that they will not work loose with vibration or normal use. Never rely on the terminal screw or the electrical cord to support weight or strain of any kind. Anchor the cord securely *ahead* of the terminals so that the strain does not reach the connection.

If screws and other minor components are replaced, make sure they are of the right size. A longer screw or a bulkier component might penetrate the insulation of a wire, causing a short to the cabinet.

If a new branch line must be installed, be sure to consult the local electrical code, as well as the National Electrical Code. Branch lines in the home are usually run with either armored cable (BX) or a nonmetallic sheath cable (Romex), as shown in Fig. 1-2.

Never replace a 15-amp fuse with a 20-amp. This is asking for trouble, because a circuit bearing a 15-amp fuse is most likely not intended to carry 20 amperes. On the other hand, when replacing electrical components in the appliance itself, never replace with a component of *lesser* value of capacity. The same is true of wiring—if part of the wire harness of an appliance must be replaced, be sure the replacement wire is the same size as the original.

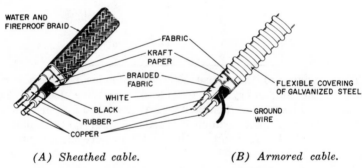

(A) Sheathed cable.   (B) Armored cable.

Fig. 1-2. Types of house-wiring cable.

TEST EQUIPMENT

Test equipment, such as an analyzer, can be of considerable aid in diagnosing the cause of trouble in an appliance. Generally speaking, the purpose of testing is to discover whether or not current is flowing through a particular component without opposition or leaks. Thus, components may be found to be "leaky" or "open." The procedure is to disconnect the component from the regular line, connect the leads from the test equipment to the component terminals, then plug in or switch on the test equipment to get a reading on the dial. A list and description of the more useful items of test equipment needed by an appliance service technician is as follows:

Ohmmeter—This serves chiefly to test electrical continuity in order to locate shorts or opens in circuits, segments of circuits, switches, thermostats, and start capacitors on motors. An ohmmeter ordinarily measures resistance; when applied between points where continuity is supposed to exist and no

Fig. 1-3. Hook-on ammeter.

meter indication is obtained, the circuit is open and the component being checked should be repaired or replaced. If the needle moves, the circuit is closed and can be considered functional (this does not apply to capacitors).

Ammeter—A hook-on ammeter (Fig. 1-3) is a convenient test instrument because it does not require disturbing the circuit to obtain a reading. Ammeters are used for measuring current flow, the reading being compared with a standard established by the appliance manufacturer.

Voltmeter—This is a necessary tool for determining high- or low-voltage conditions which may contribute to unsatisfactory performance. It can be used to measure voltage at an outlet or, by disconnecting a motor and substituting a volt-meter, the amount of voltage being delivered by the appliance wiring harness to the motor can be measured.

Wattmeter—A wattmeter helps the service technician determine how efficiently the mechanical system of an appliance is functioning. Too low readings can indicate weak or worn-out components in a circuit, such as a capacitor. Too high readings can indicate mechanical binding.

All four of the foregoing instruments may be combined into one convenient piece of test equipment, called an *analyzer* (Fig. 1-4).

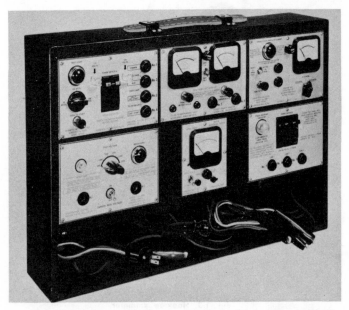

Fig. 1-4. An analyzer.   Courtesy Airserco Mfg. Co.

Continuity test light (Fig. 1-5)—This is used to discover whether or not a current is flowing through a circuit, but does not measure the amount. No light, of course, means that the circuit is dead. This device is useful in testing segments of wire harness and double-checking branch lines before disassembling the appliance.

Electrical Testing

The following discussion gives the procedure to be followed in testing the various components normally found in appliances.

14

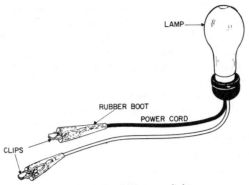

Fig. 1-5. Continuity test light.

Line voltage—Plug the leads from the appliance into the voltmeter, and the voltmeter leads into the outlet regularly used for the appliance. Turn the appliance on as well as any others connected to the same branch line.

Switches—Check with an ohmmeter for continuity across the terminals at each switch setting. *CAUTION—before making any tests with an ohmmeter, remove the power plug from the outlet to prevent damaging the instrument.*

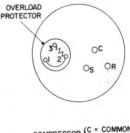

Fig. 1-6. Terminal arrangement of typical overload protector.

COMPRESSOR TERMINALS { C = COMMON
S = START
R = RUN

Overload protectors—Use a wattmeter and a jumper wire to check the overload protector on compressors (Fig. 1-6). The jumper should be connected between terminals 1 and 2 on three-terminal overloads (*A* and *B* on some compressors). If higher than the specified wattage is consumed, the overload protector is probably good *if it opens the circuit*, and some other component of the system should be suspected. If wattage consumption is normal and removal of the jumper wire stops the compressor, the protector is defective and should be replaced.

15

Thermostats—Check for continuity with an ohmmeter connected across the terminals. Remove the lead wires, turn the thermostat to its high-limit setting, and connect the ohmmeter. No reading indicates a faulty thermostat.

Start capacitors—If the motor draws excessive current or hums while starting (or does not start at all), the start capacitor may be faulty. A visual check will frequently disclose a white residue at or near the terminals, indicating a faulty capacitor. In the absence of any visual signs, the best test is to momentarily replace the old start capacitor with one of exactly the same specifications.

A capacitor can also be checked by making a resistance test; however, it must first be discharged. To do so, pull the power plug from the wall outlet and momentarily short across the capacitor terminals with a jumper wire. Set the ohmmeter on the 1-megohm scale. Take a reading across the capacitor terminals. Reverse the leads and take another reading; if the ohmmeter needle stabilizes at 30,000 ohms or less, the capacitor should be considered leaky and should be replaced.

Run capacitor—Unexplainable excessive power consumption indicates a faulty run capacitor. Make the ohmmeter test described for the start capacitor. If the needle comes almost instantly to zero and slowly returns to infinity, the capacitor is functioning properly. If the needle does not move at all, the capacitor is open. If the needle comes to rest somewhere between zero and infinity, the capacitor is leaky. In either of the latter cases, the unit should be replaced.

Relays—Excessive wattage consumption of compressors in refrigerators, freezers, and air conditioners after reaching normal run speed could indicate a relay that is not properly dropping out of the circuit after start. Low line voltage will sometimes cause the relay to "chatter." To check, short out the relay with a jumper wire across the proper terminals. (Refer to the wiring diagram on manufacturers' service literature for the correct terminals to jump.) Apply the jumper wire while the compressor is running, but for no longer than 2 or 3 seconds at a time. If the compressor runs properly during the test, a faulty relay is indicated.

Circuit lines—Use the continuity test light to check suspected lines in the circuit. For example, if a fan motor does not run, disconnect its leads and connect them to the probes of the test light. Always be sure that the appliance cycle is at the point where the inoperative component should be operating. This is usually accomplished by turning the timer dial to the proper setting.

Solenoids—Check across the terminals with an ohmmeter in the same manner as for a thermostat check.

Timers—Check across each set of contact points with an ohmmeter, the same as for switches.

PREVENTIVE MAINTENANCE

While it is not generally publicized, even in the owner's instruction manual, most appliances will require a minimum of preventive maintenance. This is particularly true of washers and dryers, whose parts generally operate faster and under greater load than other appliances. Any belt-driven appliance should be a candidate for preventive maintenance.

Sealed compressors and some washer transmissions, of course, never require lubrication, the lubricant being sealed inside the mechanical housing. However, all pulley wheels, drive wheels, cam surfaces, and other exposed mechanical parts should have regular attention, at least once a year. Large, exposed surfaces which bear on others (such as cam shafts) should be lightly coated with graphite or other suitable lubricant. Motor bearings need a drop or two of a good grade of motor oil three or four times a year. Water pumps are usually equipped with an oil wick for lubrication. This wick should be removed and soaked in turbine oil at least twice a year.

Some appliances boast "sealed" bearings on drive pulleys. Take this with a grain of salt—and a drop of oil. The best of these seals dry out after a year or two of use, permitting the lubricant to seep out. The sealed oil cap of these bearings should be pierced with an ice pick and lubricant applied regularly thereafter.

The need for lubrication is betrayed by squeaks and binding in the mechanical system. The presence of oil in drip pans, on the floor, or in other places where it should not be also indicates an investigation is necessary. Oil around a sealed compressor almost always indicates a serious failure has occurred or is imminent.

Tools

Any special tools required to accomplish servicing an appliance will be covered in the chapter dealing with the particular appliance. A set of good electrical tools and a set of mechanic's tools will, in most cases, be sufficient to accomplish the job. In addition, a wheel puller is very useful in cases where components are force-fitted together.

CHAPTER 2

REFRIGERATORS and FREEZERS

A refrigerator is any container in which food may be stored at a temperature low enough to prevent or delay the natural ripening and decaying processes of all organic matter. By this definition, both the old-fashioned window box and the icebox were true refrigerators; but there is a significant difference between these two old household appliances.

The window box was simply a large tin box, with a hinged door, secured outside the pantry window. It was used only in winter, when the cold outside air served to remove the internal heat of the food it contained. There was no insulation of any kind in the window box, because this would only have slowed down the heat dissipation.

The icebox, on the other hand, was heavily insulated. The insulation served exactly the same purpose then as it does today—to prevent, as much as possible, the entrance of heat into the interior of the cabinet.

COOLING PRINCIPLES

In both of these types of refrigerators, food is kept cold as a result of a scientific principle—heat flows from substances of higher temperature to substances of lower temperatures.

A collateral principle also comes into play—heat (or energy) cannot be destroyed, only changed. These same principles are used in the operation of today's highly sophisticated, attractive, and dependable refrigerators and freezers.

Before going into the actual operation of refrigerators and freezers, a few physical phenomena will be examined which, while not necessarily related to each other, do relate to the subject of refrigeration. Having mastered these principles, it will be easier to understand the function of the household refrigerator, as well as the air conditioner which is discussed in Chapter 8.

Cold

There is no such *thing* as cold. Just as darkness is the relative absence of light, so is cold the absence of heat. When a person says he is cold, he actually means that he feels colder than normal. The absolute absence of heat (absolute zero) is expressed on the Fahrenheit scale as *minus* 469.67°F. This means that a block of ice at 30°F is still nearly 500°F *warmer* than the cold of outer space. So it can be seen that cold, as we encounter it, is relative.

States of Matter

All matter exists in one of three states—solid, liquid, or vapor (Fig. 2-1). Iron exists as a solid in its natural state (i.e., in the state which is normal in the environment provided by our earth and atmosphere). When enough heat is applied to iron, it changes into a liquid state. If an enormous amount of heat were applied to it, as in a thermonuclear explosion, iron would vaporize.

Water is normally a liquid; normal being the temperatures ordinarily encountered in man's environment. When the temperature drops below 32°F, water freezes into its solid state.

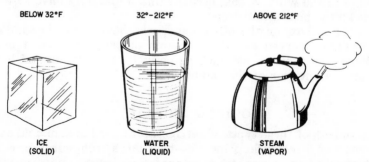

BELOW 32°F   32°–212°F   ABOVE 212°F

ICE (SOLID)   WATER (LIQUID)   STEAM (VAPOR)

Fig. 2-1. The three states of matter.

When the temperature climbs, water begins to vaporize at its surface; the vaporization rate increases as the temperature increases. When the temperature of the water reaches 212°F, vaporization takes place so fast that water begins to "boil." At temperatures above 212°F, water cannot exist at all in its liquid state, and it changes completely to a vapor.

Oxygen, a colorless, odorless gas, is found in nature in a state of vapor. However, when oxygen is compressed, it becomes a liquid.

There is no real difference between a gas and a vapor. Gas is any substance which is ordinarily found in a gaseous state; vapor is the gaseous state of any substance that is ordinarily found in a solid or liquid state.

Refrigerants

Certain substances make better refrigerants than others because they boil or vaporize at temperatures well below the desired temperature of the refrigerated space. The refrigerant *Monochlorodifluoromethane* ($CHClF_2$) (popularly known as *Refrigerant 22*, or *R-22*) vaporizes at minus 41.4°F at sea level. Thus, when liquid R-22 is suddenly introduced into an expansion chamber, it will immediately begin to boil and (as will be seen later) absorb heat from its surroundings, even if the surrounding space is already at a temperature well below the freezing point of water.

Another desirable characteristic of a good refrigerant is its ability to change readily to a liquid state when placed under compression. Refrigerants that require high pressure make it necessary to provide heavier and more expensive components. Refrigerants should also be relatively safe to handle.

Evaporation

As many readers know, evaporation is accompanied by a heat loss. When heat is added slowly (as from a stove burner) to a pot of cold water, the water becomes warmer (Fig. 2-2). This heat that can be felt and measured is called *sensible* heat. As more and more heat is gradually applied to the pot of water, it begins to steam and then to boil. If a thermometer is inserted in the water before it comes to a boil, it will be noticed that the reading will climb at a steady rate to 212°F where the water begins to boil. As soon as boiling takes place, however, the reading will remain at 212°F, going no higher until all the water has boiled away.

However, heat was being applied to the pot even after the water had begun to boil. What happened to all this heat during this period? The answer is that the heat was being transformed into energy by the water to effect the change of state from a liquid to a vapor. This change of state requires a great deal of energy to increase the relatively sluggish movement of the water molecules to the accelerated movement required of a vapor. So, instead of registering any further increase in temperature (sensible heat), the water uses up the heat as energy, which does not register on a thermometer.

The same thing takes place as a drop of water evaporates on your arm. The additional energy required to change the mole-

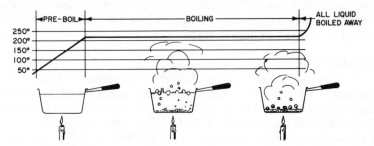

Fig. 2-2. Energy absorption by water during a change of state.

cules of water into a vapor state comes from the surrounding area so that your skin feels cool until all the water evaporates.

The heat used by a substance changing from one state to another is called *latent* heat. In changing from a liquid to a vapor, the heat used up is called *latent heat of evaporation.* In changing from a solid to a liquid, the heat is called *latent heat of fusion.*

This phenomenon is the basic principle of refrigeration as it is used in present day refrigerators and air conditioners.

Vapor Pressure

All gases and vapors exert equal pressure in all directions. The molecules they contain are constantly bombarding their confining vessels with billions of collisions per second. If more vapor is added to a vessel (Fig. 2-3), the number of molecules it contains is increased, thereby increasing the number of molecular collisions. Similarly, if the volume of a vessel is reduced (Fig. 2-4) as in the cylinder of a compressor, the number of molecular bombardments per square inch of the confining vessel is increased. This also raises the pressure of the vapor, and it is said to be under *compression.*

The more a vapor is compressed, the less distance its molecules will travel before colliding with each other or with the

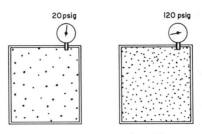

Fig. 2-3. Increasing pressure by adding vapor.

sides of the confining vessel. If the molecules travel shorter distances, they need less energy than for longer distances. (Again, it must be remembered that heat and energy cannot be destroyed—only changed.) Therefore the energy no longer needed by the molecules is released in the form of sensible heat.

The opposite is also true. If the volume of the vessel and the amount of vapor it contains remain unchanged, its pressure can be increased by adding heat to the vessel.

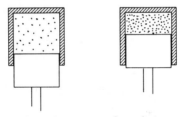

Fig. 2-4. Increasing pressure by reducing volume.

This relationship between the pressure and the temperature of a particular vapor never changes (Fig. 2-5). In the case of R-12, for instance, if the vapor temperature reads 25°F, the pressure of the vapor will be at exactly 24.6 psig (pounds per square inch gauge). If some of the vapor in the container were to be released so that the pressure would drop to 21 psig, the vapor temperature would quickly drop to 20°F.

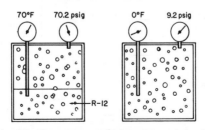

Fig. 2-5. Vapor pressure/temperature relationship.

The constant, predictable relationship of pressure to temperature and vice versa is extremely valuable knowledge to a refrigeration serviceman in checking performance and in diagnosing the cause of trouble in a system. By taking temperature/pressure readings and comparing them with norms established by the manufacturer of a refrigerator, freezer, or air conditioner, the serviceman can very quickly determine the cause of a failure in the system.

HOW A REFRIGERATOR WORKS

A refrigeration system can be summed up in a few words. It is a mechanical system of tubes of varying inside diameter through which is pumped a refrigerant under alternating high and low pressure. In the "high side" of the system (Fig. 2-6), the refrigerant is under compression, causing it to give up its heat and condense to a liquid. The greater part of the high side is separate from the refrigerated space so that heat is discharged outside the cabinet. In the "low side" of the system (inside the refrigerator cabinet), the liquid refrigerant ex-

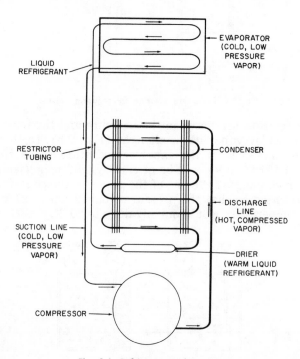

Fig. 2-6. Refrigerator schematic.

pands to a vapor, absorbing heat and transforming it into the necessary energy required for vaporization. Repeated circulation of the refrigerant will gradually cool down the refrigerated space to the desired temperature.

Now, each of the components of a refrigeration system will be examined in detail. (Start at the compressor in Fig. 2-6 and read the schematic diagram counterclockwise.)

The *compressor* receives hot refrigerant vapor from the *suction line* in the low side, compresses it, and sends it through the *discharge line* into the *condenser*. The condenser is located outside the refrigerated space, usually at the back of the cabinet. When the refrigerant vapor enters the condenser, it contains heat which it has absorbed in two forms—heat as energy which is causing increased movement of the molecules in the vapor, and sensible heat which it has absorbed in the later passes of the evaporator, as well as from the action of the compressor itself.

The condenser on most refrigerators and freezers is so designed and located that a natural draft of ambient (or room) air is generated around and through the fins which surround the condenser tubing. This flow of air may be augmented by a condenser fan in some models. The molecules of vapor, being now compressed into a much smaller space, no longer require the great amounts of energy they possessed. This energy is now transformed back into sensible heat, along with the sensible heat contained by the vapor which it absorbed from the later passes of the evaporator and from the compressor.

The heat contained in the vapor (obeying the law that heat passes from substances of higher temperature to substances of lower temperature) passes into the fins of the condenser, from which it passes to the cooler air flowing past the fins. When the refrigerant vapor reaches the last passes (a pass is a turn of the copper tubing) of the condenser, it has become cool enough to condense to a liquid.

From the condenser, the liquid refrigerant passes into the *liquid line* and back into the refrigerator cabinet. Here, it enters the *restrictor*, a length of copper tubing which acts like a dam to separate the high side of the system from the low side. Having an inside diameter of only a few hundredths of an inch, the restrictor allows only a small flow of liquid refrigerant to enter the evaporator.

In the *evaporator*, which has tubing of much larger diameter, the liquid refrigerant is suddenly able to expand. In order to do so, it must "borrow" energy from its surroundings to motivate the molecules to travel the greater distances involved. The energy it needs is present in the form of sensible heat in the air immediately surrounding the fins and coils that make up the evaporator. The refrigerant traveling through the evaporator absorbs more and more of the sensible heat surrounding it until it completely evaporates (Fig. 2-7).

The sensible temperature of the refrigerant liquid and vapor has not been raised by even 1 degree until the point is reached in the vaporization process where all the liquid refrigerant boils away. This is due to the fact that all the sensible heat it has absorbed up to this point has been latent heat of evapora-

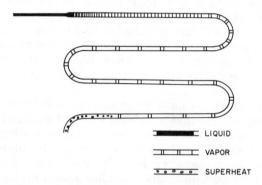

LIQUID

VAPOR

SUPERHEAT

Fig. 2-7. Three stages of refrigerant in cooling tubes.

tion—i.e., heat which has been transformed into energy. However, toward the end of its travel in the evaporator, where complete vaporization has taken place, the refrigerant vapor now begins to grow warmer since it no longer needs the energy. It is now called *superheated vapor,* or *superheat.* This simply means that the vapor is at a temperature higher than that required for vaporization. The hot refrigerant vapor now passes into the suction line, and once again into the compressor, where the cycle starts over again.

A certain amount of superheat is provided for in a refrigeration system. This is to prevent the possibility of any unvaporized (liquid) refrigerant from entering the compressor. Since liquids are largely incompressible, liquid in the compressor would cause loud knocking noises and possible damage to the delicate leaf valves inside.

The evaporator is located near the top of the cabinet interior in all refrigerators and freezers. As the air surrounding the evaporator gives up its heat, it tends to sink to the bottom of the cabinet (cold air sinks, warm air rises). This stirs up the air at the bottom, displacing it so that it rises to the top

(Fig. 2-8). Thus, a continuous circulation of the air is always taking place within the cabinet.

Since heat flows from substances of higher temperature to substances of lower temperature, any object at room temperature which is placed within the refrigerator will soon give up its own heat to the cooler air in the cabinet. This air in turn releases its heat to the energy-starved refrigerant liquid in the evaporator. The continuous cycling of the refrigerant through the evaporator gradually cools the interior of the refrigerator or freezer (and all its contents) to the desired temperature.

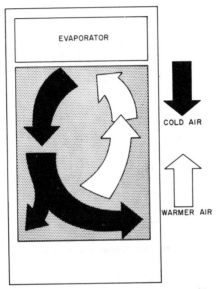

Fig. 2-8. Air circulation within refrigerator cabinet.

The Compressor

The heart of a refrigeration system is the motor compressor. Most, if not all, refrigeration systems are of the "closed" type, which is to say that the compressor pump and the electric motor that powers it are all contained in a sealed shell through which the refrigerant also travels.

The compressor is simply a pump designed to handle vapor through a system of leaf valves. Power for the pump is obtained through an electric motor mounted within the same shell, which is sealed to prevent the entrance of dirt, outside air, and moisture. A suction-line inlet through which refrigerant vapor is admitted is located somewhere near the top of the compressor housing. In most compressors, the hot vapor is free to travel throughout the interior of the compressor and motor housing.

Another suction inlet is located inside the housing, above the oil reservoir level. This inlet leads the hot vapor into the compressor cylinder (through an inlet valve) where it is compressed and led into the discharge line and out of the housing. Oil for lubrication of the piston and other moving parts is also present in the interior of the housing, where some of it may circulate freely through the refrigeration system, serving to lubricate needle valves and other controls. The bulk of the oil, however, remains in the compressor housing.

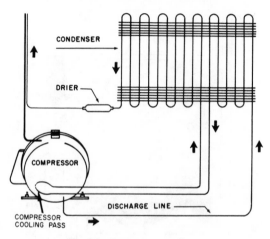

Fig. 2-9. Compressor cooling.

A pass of the condenser is introduced into the compressor housing, in some units, which causes the cooled refrigerant liquid to aid in cooling the interior of the compressor (Fig. 2-9). This pass occurs before the refrigerant reaches the half-way mark in its travel through the condenser so that if it starts to vaporize as it passes through the warm compressor, it has another opportunity to liquefy through the remaining passes of the condenser.

In order to prevent damage to the compressor due to an overload or some other condition which would put a heavy drain on the current supplied to the motor, an overload protector (Fig. 2-10) is introduced into the circuit. This overload protector is usually a bimetal disc made of two metals having different heat coefficients. At normal temperatures, the metal discs are curved parabolically so that the current flows without interruption through them. If a surge of electricity occurs (as in an overloaded condition), the bi-metal discs expand at different rates, causing them to snap into a curve opposite to the normal one. This opens the contacts and the circuit to the motor, stopping the compressor. When the discs cool, they return to their normal form, and the current is permitted to flow again. (For a complete discussion of the types of motors used in refrigerator compressors, see Chapter 10.)

Controls

It is obvious that if the refrigerant were allowed to cycle without interruption, it would eventually bring the temperature of the interior down to its own temperature, which might be as low as minus 40°F at 0.6 psig. This would be far too cold for proper storage of refrigerated foods.

The principle means of controlling the temperature of the interior is by cycling the motor compressor on and off. As long as the motor compressor is not operating, the refrigerant is permitted to remain at a uniform pressure throughout the system, and no refrigeration takes place.

A *thermostat* (Fig. 2-11), accomplishes the compressor cycling by its unique ability to sense changes in temperature. This device is nothing more than a hollow tube with a bulb at one end and an expanding and contracting bellows at the other. This assembly is filled with a small amount of the refrigerant

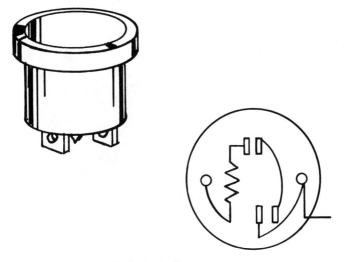

Fig. 2-10. Overload protector.

used in the main refrigerating system. The sensing bulb is placed in the evaporator so that it responds to temperature changes occurring at the source of the cold air. With the compressor running, the evaporator becomes colder, and the refrigerant in the sensing bulb contracts, reducing the pressure at the bellows end. A spring overcomes the expansion of the bellows, and it begins to collapse. At a predetermined point in the travel of the bellows another spring mechanism causes an electric switch to snap open, interrupting the flow of current to the compressor (Fig. 2-12).

With the compressor stopped, a gradual warm up occurs in the evaporator as heat from the room penetrates the cabinet. This causes the refrigerant vapor in the sensing bulb to expand, pushing the bellows against the force of the spring. At the upper end of the range of temperatures prescribed for the thermostat, the spring mechanism of the electric switch forces the contacts to snap closed, and electricity flows to the compressor, causing it to start.

Electrical switches in any household appliance are manufactured to open and close with a positive action. If the contacts were permitted to approach each other slowly, they would reach a point where the electricity would jump the short distance between them, accompanied by a hot spark. This condition, called *arcing*, would soon damage the contacts if allowed to occur often enough. The snap provided by the spring mechanism minimizes this condition.

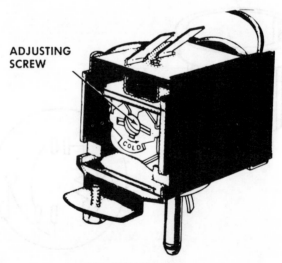

Fig. 2-11. Thermostat.

Thermostats may be set through two main adjustments—the *range* and *differential*. The range of a thermostat is set by the manufacturer and should only be adjusted by qualified servicemen. It is usually accomplished by means of a screw located beneath the differential knob.

Range determines the cut-in and cut-out temperatures at which the compressor will cycle on and off. Extreme changes in the adjustment may cause the refrigerator to cycle on and off through a range of temperature wholly inadequate for proper food storage.

The differential adjustment is intended for use by the customer and is accomplished by turning a numbered dial. The numbers usually have no relationship to any actual temperature, but are merely used for reference. The differential setting will raise or lower the cut-out temperature only; it does not affect the cut-in temperature, which is usually fixed at from 34°F to 39°F. This insures that interior temperatures in the refrigerator will not fall below the point necessary for proper food storage, and on automatic defrost models, that defrosting will take place on schedule.

The effect of a low-temperature setting of the differential knob is to cause the compressor to run for a longer period of time before cut-out, and for shorter periods at the higher temperature settings.

One important function of the range adjustment is to compensate for different altitudes. As mentioned previously, the

Fig. 2-12. Compressor control switch.

pressure of a vapor is directly related to its boiling point. The higher the altitude, the lower the atmospheric pressure becomes. This is also true of the vapor pressure in the refrigeration system. It is necessary, therefore, to adjust the range of the thermostat to compensate for the difference in the boiling point of the refrigerant vapor. Table 2-1 gives typical adjustments necessary for different altitudes above sea level.

Table 2-1. Adjustment of Range Screw for Various Altitudes

Altitude Above Sea Level	Range Screw Adjustment
(In feet)	(Number of turns clockwise)*
1,000	None
2,000	¼
4,000	½
6,000	¾
8,000	One full turn

* Some thermostats are constructed so that the adjustment must be turned counterclockwise—check manufacturer's literature for the exact procedure.

DEFROSTING

When warm air passes over a cool object, the air in contact with the object gives up its moisture in the form of droplets of water. The more humid the air and the greater the contrast of temperature between the air and the object, the more rapid is the formation of the condensate.

A refrigerator evaporator, the ice trays, cooling plate, and other components nearby are in a very cold state. When the refrigerator door is opened, a mass of warm air is admitted into the interior of the cabinet. This air passing over the cold components releases its moisture in the form of water. The water then freezes on the cold component, eventually building up a thick coating of frost. The more often the refrigerator door is opened and the more humid and warm the air which is admitted to the interior, the more rapidly will frost form on the evaporator.

Frost hampers the free exchange of heat between the air in the cabinet interior, evaporator fins, and coils so that it must be removed periodically; the removal process is called defrosting.

Many refrigerators are still manufactured with no defrosting mechanism. In these models the customer merely switches off the refrigerator and places a pan of warm water under the evaporator until the ice melts and drains off into the pan.

The evaporator surfaces are then wiped clean and dry, and the refrigerator switched on again to resume operation.

In other models, defrosting is accomplished semiautomatically. The defrost switch is turned to the Defrost position, which opens the circuit to the compressor. Warm water placed in a pan under the evaporator may be used to melt the frost, or the customer may elect to let defrosting proceed with no further attention. When the evaporator has reached a predetermined high and all ice has melted off the surfaces, the circuit to the compressor is closed automatically by means of a temperature-sensing thermostat, and the refrigerator resumes normal operation of its own accord.

Fully automatic defrosting, which is called by a variety of names, is intended more to prevent frost from forming than to remove it once it has formed. The *initiation* of the defrost cycle is accomplished in one of two ways. In the first method, a cam on the bottom of the refrigerator door trips a counter mechanism (Fig. 2-13). When the door has been opened and closed a predetermined number of times, the counter closes a defrost-cycle circuit and defrosting begins.

In the second method, an automatic timer (Fig. 2-14) is energized each time the compressor operates. The timer functions only during the period of compressor operation. After about 12 hours of accumulated running time, a spring mechanism is actuated and the defrost cycle circuit is closed.

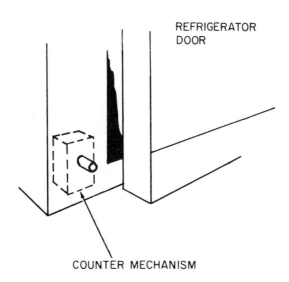

REFRIGERATOR DOOR

COUNTER MECHANISM

Fig. 2-13. A method of initiating a defrost cycle.

A less frequently used method of initiating the defrost cycle depends on the actual physical build-up of frost. A spring-loaded button is gradually pushed toward a contact by the increasing thickness of ice forming on the evaporator. When it has reached a predetermined thickness, the button trips a spring mechanism, which in turn causes the defrost-cycle circuit to close. Since this method depends on the thickness of the ice, it cannot in truth be called a "no-frost" or "frost-free" system.

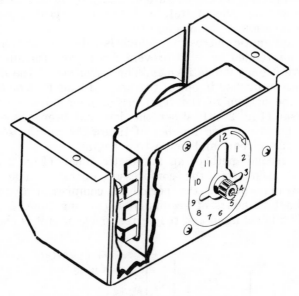

Fig. 2-14. Defrost circuit energization.

The actual process of defrosting can also be accomplished in several ways. In the first of two of the more popular ways, a heating coil is employed directly beneath the evaporator. As the defrost cycle is initiated, the compressor circuit is opened and the heater-coil circuit closed. The heater, giving off intense heat for a short period, quickly melts the ice without affecting the interior temperature of the cabinet too drastically.

As the ice melts, the resultant water drips into a drain pan, through drain channels in the walls of the refrigerator and into a condensate pan beneath the condenser. Here, it is permitted to evaporate into room air, the process being sometimes hastened by either a condenser fan, heater coil, or both.

When the temperature of the refrigerator cabinet reaches a predetermined high (approximately 45°F), a defrost term-

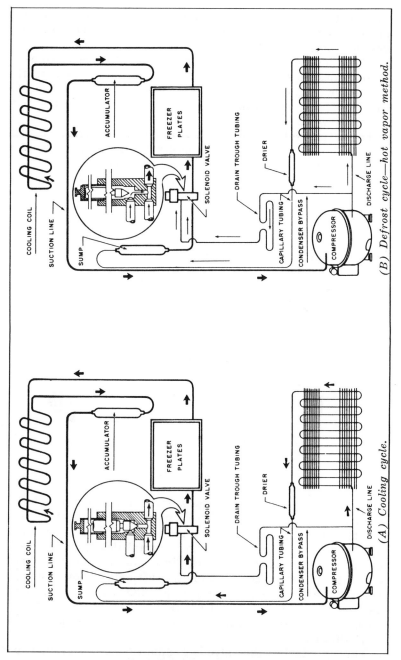

Fig. 2-15. Refrigerator schematic.

inating thermostat closes the circuit to the compressor and opens the circuit to the heater coil. The refrigerator now resumes normal operation.

The other method of defrosting, and one that seems to be in more widespread use, causes the refrigerant to by-pass the condenser temporarily so that the evaporator, instead of cooling the space, now functions exactly the same as the condenser (Fig. 2-15).

The defrost initiator mechanism energizes a defrost solenoid valve. This valve (Fig. 2-16) offers the refrigerant flow a choice of two channels. In the closed position (normal refrig-

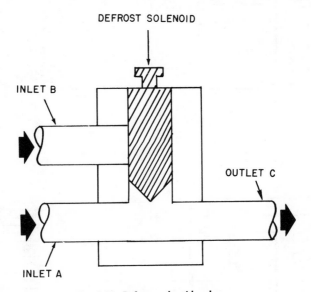

Fig. 2-16. Defrost solenoid valve.

eration) the refrigerant travels from Inlet A through the valve and out at C. In the Defrost position, the initiator mechanism causes the plunger to be pulled upward. This opens an additional inlet at B, and the refrigerant flow is now able to enter the valve at both A and B. Since flow is through the path of least resistance, the bulk of the refrigerant flows through B and out at C, thus effectively by-passing the condenser. Condenser flow, however, is not entirely restricted, since dangerously high pressures would be built up in the condenser if this were the case.

The net effect of the valve is to admit hot refrigerant vapor to the evaporator for a short period of time. Since vapor normally leaves the compressor at approximately 120°F, the thin film of ice which may have formed on the evaporator since the last defrost cycle quickly melts away.

As in the heater-coil defrost cycle, a defrost terminating thermostat breaks the circuit to the solenoid valve when a predetermined high has been reached, and the refrigerant vapor proceeds on its normal course through the condenser and restrictor tubing.

REFRIGERATOR/FREEZER COMBINATIONS

Many popular models contain two separate compartments, each heavily insulated from the other. Each compartment operates at a different temperature, the refrigerator section being maintained at a customer-selected temperature which may range from 34°F to 42°F, while the temperature in the freezer section is normally kept at approximately 0°F. This

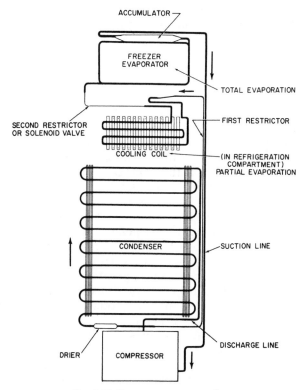

Fig. 2-17. Two-compartment cooling.

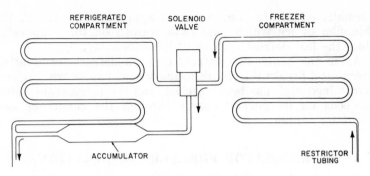

ACCUMULATOR   RESTRICTOR TUBING

Fig. 2-18. Earlier method of temperature-difference control.

temperature difference is achieved in several ways in existing refrigerator/freezers.

While it may appear that a refrigerator/freezer combination has two separate evaporators, it is actually only one unit, with some of its passes in the freezer section and some in the refrigerator section (Fig. 2-17). In earlier model refrigerators, the difference in temperature in the two compartments was achieved through the use of a solenoid valve and a by-pass refrigerant-flow circuit (Fig. 2-18). When the refrigerator compartment temperature reached a predetermined low, the solenoid valve was energized by an electrical circuit closed through a sensing thermostat in the refrigeration section. The valve diverted the flow of refrigerant, by-passing the refrigerator compartment passes of the evaporator so that the refrigerant traveled only through the freezer section passes.

In another method, a differential pressure-control (DPC) valve is employed (Fig. 2-19). The DPC valve is located in the evaporator passes between the refrigerator and the freezer compartments. Just ahead of the refrigerator evaporator, the usual restrictor tubing causes a moderate pressure drop in the first section of the evaporator, permitting only a portion of the refrigerant to boil, but maintaining most of the refrigerant in a liquid state until it reaches the DPC valve. At this point, the pressure drop becomes much greater, causing the refrigerant boiling point to drop to an equivalent temperature of minus 5°F (obeying the positive relationship between the pressure of a vapor and its temperature). Control of the DPC valve is achieved by hand settings on a dial, which varies the amount of flow obstruction, increasing or decreasing the drop in pressure to achieve a variety of temperatures.

Any refrigerant which may emerge from the evaporator still in a liquid state is collected in an accumulator, where it continues to vaporize. The outlet of the accumulator leading to the suction line is located above the level of any liquid it may contain, thus preventing liquid from reaching the compressor.

The third method of achieving a difference in temperature between the freezer and refrigerator sections is by varying

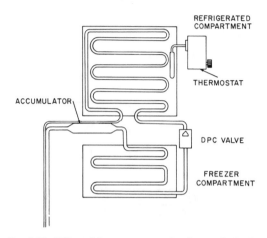

Fig. 2-19. Differential pressure-control valve method of two-compartment cooling.

the evaporator surface area in the two compartments (Fig. 2-20). In this method, a balance is achieved by the engineer in the design of the system, taking into account the volume of the spaces to be refrigerated. A plate is mounted on the wall of the refrigerator compartment; this plate usually consists of two pieces of metal pressed together in such a way that channels are left open between the two through which the refrigerant may travel. The size of the plate in relation to the cubic volume to be refrigerated is carefully calculated so that even though the temperature at any one point on the surface of the plate reaches 0°F, the average temperature of the refrigerated space remains at a constant 38°F to 42°F.

The latter method seems to be the one most favored in modern refrigerators because of its simplicity in operation, and because additional, trouble-prone components are not required.

Convertible Refrigerator/Freezers

Some models on the market are described as "convertible," which is to say that the freezer compartment may be converted

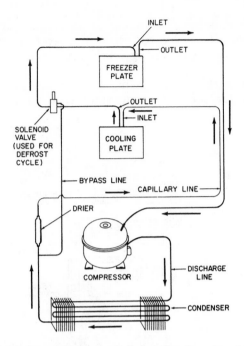

INLET

OUTLET

FREEZER
PLATE

OUTLET

INLET

SOLENOID
VALVE
(USED FOR
DEFROST
CYCLE)

COOLING
PLATE

BYPASS LINE

CAPILLARY LINE

DRIER

DISCHARGE
LINE

COMPRESSOR

CONDENSER

Fig. 2-20. Evaporator area method of cooling two compartments.

into an ordinary refrigerated section in the event of a temporary demand for more space. This is accomplished by having a "split evaporator" in the freezer section. When the entire evaporator is used, the space is cooled to the zero temperature required for freezer storage. When only a portion of the evaporator is used, however, the space is cooled down to the 34°F to 42°F range normally encountered in a refrigerator (Fig. 2-21).

A solenoid valve is placed in the refrigerant line between the restrictor and the evaporator. This valve is energized by a current which may be turned on and off by the Convertible-Operation switch. This switch is operated by the customer.

With the switch in the Normal (freezer) position, the solenoid valve remains open due to the force of the retaining spring acting on the valve plunger. The refrigerant is permitted to flow through the valve and into a series of passes in the evaporator. After emerging from the first series of passes, it travels through the valve a second time and then into a second series of evaporator passes.

With the switch in the Convertible position, the flow of refrigerant is turned back at the valve, by-passing the first series of evaporator passes and flowing only through the second series. The ice trays are located near the second series of passes and are contained in a compartment separated from the rest of the space in the freezer section by an insulated partition. The diameter of the tubing and the surface area of both sections of the evaporator are carefully prescribed in the design of the system so that the interior temperature is maintained

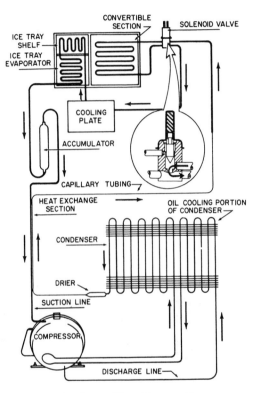

Fig. 2-21. Convertible refrigerator/freezer.

at the correct levels required for fresh foods when in the Convertible position, and is lowered to the necessary zero cold when in the Freezer position.

Some freezers are also known as "convertibles." In this type, a separate compartment is switched to ordinary refrigeration to take care of any overflow that may occur in the household refrigerator during holiday preparations and other temporary situations. The conversion is accomplished in the same manner as for convertible refrigerator/freezers.

POSITION (1)
SWITCH 1 OPEN
SWITCH 2 OPEN

POSITION (2)
SWITCH 1 CLOSED
SWITCH 2 OPEN

POSITION (3)
SWITCH 1 CLOSED
SWITCH 2 CLOSED

POSITION (4)
SWITCH 1 CLOSED
SWITCH 2 OPEN

Fig. 2-22. Leaf-spring mounted control switches.

Automatic Ice Makers

Many late model refrigerators feature a device that makes ice cubes, maintaining a constant supply automatically. The ice maker is a combination of electrical and mechanical operations. One such device has five distinct parts to its cycle: the freeze, the release, the ejection, the sweep and the water fill.

To follow the sequence of operations in the cycle, we begin with the ice cube making mold, which supplies "cubes" that are actually cylindrical in shape. Since the ice-making apparatus is enclosed in the freezer portion of the refrigerator, as soon as water is introduced into the molds, freezing begins to take place. When the cubes are frozen hard (temperature readings of 16°F) a thermostat sensor causes the thermostat contacts to close, initiating the release part of the cycle.

Now a heater coil and the ice-maker power-motor are energized. The motor begins to rotate, but is prevented from doing so by the sticking of the frozen cubes. In the meantime, the heater is acting to loosen the cubes from their molds. As soon as the motor is able to overcome the sticking of the cubes, ejection begins as eject levers lift the individual cubes out of the molds. The sweep cycle now begins as a rake sweeps over the molds, carrying the cubes with it into a receptacle tray.

When sweeping has been accomplished, the water fill action begins with the energizing of a solenoid valve controlling the flow and interruption of water into the molds. The cycle will continue until the ice receptacle tray is filled, tripping a spring-loaded micro switch actuated by the weight of the ice cubes. Control of the ice-making device described above is accomplished by means of a four-position switch (Fig. 2-22). A series of leaf-spring mounted contacts interacts under the influence of an eccentrically mounted cam so that, in different degrees of rotation of the cam, different contacts are closed and opened to actuate separate parts of the cycle.

Most of the servicing problems associated with an ice-making device will be caused by a defective cam switch. However, most manufacturers recommend unit-for-unit replacement of the ice makers, rather than attempted repairs.

Miscellaneous Components

Dryer—Water will affect the efficiency of a refrigeration system because it will not vaporize at the pressures and temperatures associated with refrigerants, but will pass through in a liquid or even a frozen state. Since liquids are incompressible, any water in the system will overload the motor compressor and may even damage the valves and other controls, as was mentioned previously. Only 10 or 12 parts of water *per million parts of refrigerant* can be tolerated in a refrigeration system.

Dryers (Fig. 2-20) are introduced into the refrigerant line between the condenser and the capillary to extract any water or other impurities that may be present. The dryer contains activated alumina, silica gel, calcium sulphate, or other dehydrating agents with an affinity for water. As the refrigerant flows through the dryer, the water and other impurities it may contain are trapped and held.

Heat exchanger—Usually not a component as such in a household refrigerator, the heat exchanger is simply the meeting of the suction and discharge lines, taped or soldered together in intimate contact for part of their travel (Fig. 2-23). The (relatively) warm refrigerant liquid passing through the capillary on its way to the evaporator gives up some of its heat to the cooler refrigerant vapor in the suction line. This does two things—(1) it increases the pressure of the vapor in the suction line, thereby improving the efficiency of the compressor; and (2) it acts as extra insurance that the liquid refrigerant will not vaporize prematurely before it enters the capillary and the evaporator.

Accumulator—This component serves as a vessel for any unevaporated liquid emerging from the evaporator. It is par-

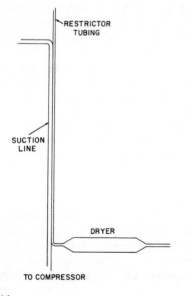

Fig. 2-23. Heat exchanger.

ticularly useful in split evaporators where only part of the evaporator is in use, as in a convertible refrigerator/freezer.

The outlet from the accumulator, also called a *header*, is located above the surface of any liquid it may contain, passing only vapor into the suction line.

Cabinet Construction

Refrigerator and freezer cabinets usually consist of two pieces—an inner "tank" or liner, and an outer shell, the space between them being filled with an insulating material. The inner liner is usually made of sheet steel and supports the various components of the system. Recently, some manufacturers have switched to liners made of high-impact Polystyrene, or similar material, to which is bonded a plastic foam insulation. It is important to handle these liners carefully when servicing the appliance, particularly in the case of freezers. In a plastic-lined freezer, the evaporator tubing is imbedded in the foam insulation, making it impossible to repair any punctures of the tubing that may occur. In such cases, the entire liner must be replaced.

The outer shell of the cabinet is usually made of heavy gauge steel, coated on both sides with a bonding material, and then sprayed with two coats of wet enamel on the outside and one coat inside. The entire assembly is then baked, resulting in a hard, lustrous finish that will withstand a great deal of abuse.

Many of the modern "top of the line" refrigerators and freezers make use of a magnetic gasket around the entire circumference of the door. This eliminates the troublesome latch assembly and provides a more positive seal against the entrance of warm air into the interior. It is simply a rubber or Neoprene tube having a special cross section, with full-length magnets contained inside (Fig. 2-24.) The magnets run across the top, bottom, and handle side of the door. Sponge rubber in the gasket at the door handle side helps to cushion the shock of closing, as well as provide a tighter air seal.

Freezers

Freezers, of course, work on exactly the same principle as refrigerators, with the exception that the temperatures employed are about 40°F lower than those in a typical refrigerator. Some freezers provide two settings, Sharp Freeze, and Frozen Food Storage. The Sharp Freeze position of the operating dial simply cycles the compressor to run continuously until the customer returns the dial to Frozen Storage, the normal

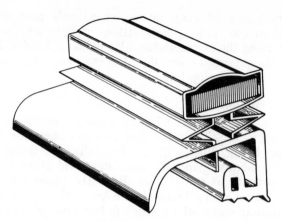

Fig. 2-24. Magnetic door gasket.

setting. Temperatures inside the cabinet during Sharp Freeze will fall to minus 20°F or below, depending on how long the compressor is permitted to operate. Normal operation of a freezer maintains an inside temperature of approximately 0°F, and is accomplished by the cycling on and off of the compressor, as energized by a regulating thermostat.

Some of the main differences between freezers and refrigerators are as follows:

Defrost—Many freezers do not provide any kind of defrost mechanism, since frost builds up much more slowly due to the less-frequent opening as compared to the normal refrigerator. It is only necessary to defrost most freezers three or four times a year under normal usage. When defrosting is provided for, it is usually of the No-Frost or Frost-Free type, which actually prevents the build-up of frost. Defrosting is usually initiated by a clock-timer, and occurs no more often than once a day. In some freezers, the defrost period is timed to occur in the middle of the night in order to reduce the chance of any food spoilage. A fan is usually provided which circulates interior air to hasten the process in the crowded interior. Defrosting is usually accomplished by the hot-vapor method, by-passing the condenser and restrictor, as in refrigerators.

Evaporator—The evaporator in a freezer usually takes the form of a series of "wrapper" coils which are imbedded in the space between the liner and the outer shell (Fig. 2-25). This arrangement ensures the even distribution of zero cold throughout the roomy cabinet interior.

Warning signal—Since a failure in the electrical system or at the power source could mean the spoilage of several hundred

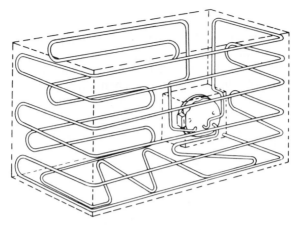

Fig. 2-25. Freezer evaporator.

dollars worth of food, most freezers provide a warning signal. This device is powered by either a dry-cell battery, or by a self-charging wet cell, and is energized whenever the compressor circuit is interrupted from normal functioning. The warning signal may be either a bell, a buzzer, or a flashing red light. A typical circuit is shown in Fig. 2-26.

Fig. 2-26. Freezer warning signal.

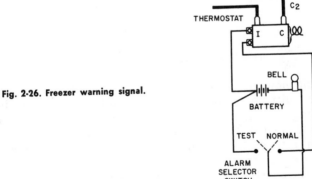

ELECTRICAL SYSTEM

Most household refrigerators run on 110-volt, 60-cycle, single-phase AC, such as commonly supplied to homes in the United States. A simplified wiring diagram for a single-temperature, single-door refrigerator is shown in Fig. 2-27. Note how the compressor circuit may be completely disconnected from the main refrigerator circuit by a service-cord plug.

Current flows through the door-light switch to the interior electric lamp and to one set of contacts at the thermostat. The second wire of the power cord feeds current directly to the same contact on the thermostat. When the contact is closed, current is permitted to flow to the motor compressor through the motor-compressor service cord.

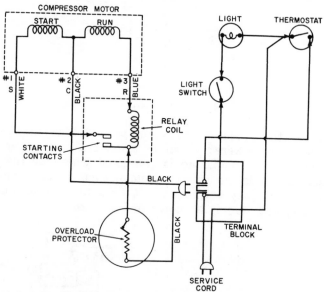

Fig. 2-27. Simple refrigerator wiring diagram.

Current now flows to the overload protector, and under normal conditions, is uninterrupted. Should a current-drain or high-voltage condition occur, the contacts would be broken and the circuit opened. When the overload condition subsides, the protector returns to its normal position, and the current is again permitted to flow.

From the overload, current flows through the relay. Electric motors of the single-phase type require help in starting, either through a start winding in the motor stator itself, or by the use of an electrolytic start capacitor. Whichever method is used, the relay serves to keep it in the circuit long enough to over-come the start inertia. When run speed has been attained, the relay disconnects the starting circuit. Fig. 2-27 shows a motor in which a start winding is used instead of a start capacitor.

There are two types of relays—*voltage* and *current*. The voltage type (Fig. 2-28) is used on capacitor-start motors only. Its contacts are normally closed so that in the first few seconds at the start, both the relay and the start capacitor are in the

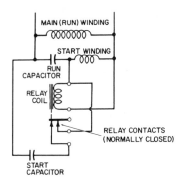

Fig. 2-28. Voltage relay.

circuit. As the motor picks up speed, the current through the relay coil increases until, at about 85% of running speed, it is strong enough to overcome the normally closed relay contacts, and the circuit to the start capacitor is opened. The motor start winding stays in the circuit.

In the current-type relay (Fig. 2-29) the contacts are normally open. The instantaneous surge of current at the start

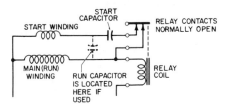

Fig. 2-29. Current relay

actuates an armature or plunger within the relay coil, which closes the start-winding circuit and the motor starts. When the motor reaches its normal-run speed (in about 3 seconds), the current drops to normal. The weight of the plunger now overcomes the magnetic force of the coil, and the start winding (or start capacitor, if one is used) is disconnected from the circuit. Current relays may be used without start capacitors, hence are ideal for the split-phase start, induction-run motors which are usually found in household refrigerators.

PERFORMANCE CHECKS

There are two ways to check the performance of a refrigerator or freezer (or any major appliance run by electricity). The first is a mechanical check, the second is an electrical test; both methods should be used in diagnosing the source of trouble in a refrigeration system.

Mechanical Checks

Visual—Check all components for visible signs of damage or wear (such as kinks, nicks, or breaks in refrigerant tubing), excessive frost on cold components, unevaporated water in drain pans, signs of compressor burn out, the presence of oil in or near the compressor, and other abnormal conditions. One of the most common causes of inefficient operation is dirt and dust clogging the condenser tubing and fins.

The experienced serviceman can also learn something from the *feel* of discharge and suction lines. The discharge line should feel hot to the touch, but not too hot to handle. The suction line should feel tepid. Cold spots along liquid lines usually mean an obstruction in the line, which is also betrayed by sweating *ahead* of any possible obstruction.

Temperature check—The interior of the cabinet may be checked for proper temperature by using a thermometer with a range above 32°F. First wash the tip thoroughly in warm water and soap. Select a container of liquid or a mass of food such as a loaf of bread which has been stored in the refrigerator for at least 12 hours prior to the check. Immerse, or bury, the tip of the thermometer so that it reaches the center of the liquid or food and close the refrigerator door. Wait a few minutes for the indicator to stabilize, then read the temperature while the tip is still immersed. Do not make the temperature check with food that has been stored in or near the evaporator, but instead select that which is near the center of the refrigerated space.

Running-time check—There are so many variables involved in the length of time that a compressor is cycled on that it is hardly worth the effort to make a running-time check. Room temperature, humidity, how recently a warm mass of food was put away, and the differential setting of the thermostat all have an effect on running time. In addition, some of the automatic defrost or frost-free refrigerators run so nearly continuously that a serviceman would have to waste 20 or 30 minutes sitting idly by waiting for the compressor to cycle off. In most cases, manufacturers have discontinued giving running times averages in service literature. Excessive running time, therefore, is not of itself a sign of system failure.

However, if a running-time check must be made, follow this procedure. First, make sure that no one opens the refrigerator door for at least an hour before the check is to be made. Take careful average readings of room air temperature (dry bulb) at the refrigerator location. If possible, take a sling psychrometer reading (wet bulb) to get the relative humidity. Now take several readings of the length of time the compressor runs, as well as the "off" intervals. Strike an average of both, and compare with average running times given in service literature for the dry and wet bulb ambients closest to those obtained in the room.

Door-gasket seal test—The tightness of the door seal can be checked by placing a dollar bill between the gasket and the cabinet and closing the door with normal force. Now try to pull the dollar bill straight out. There should be at least a slight drag. Try the same test at various places all around the door, including the hinge side. If there is no drag anywhere around the door, the gasket should be replaced. If no drag occurs only at the handle side of the door, adjustment of the latch and/or strike is indicated. Follow the manufacturers' recommended procedure for adjustment of individual models.

Leak test—Modern refrigerants are colorless and odorless, and are therefore almost impossible to detect by sight or smell. One of the surest signs of a refrigerant leak is the presence of oil at any point in the system. Oil mixes intimately with refrigerant liquid and vapor and is present throughout the interior of the tubing and components. Any refrigerant leak is therefore sure to be accompanied by some oil.

A *Hallide* leak detector (Fig. 2-30) or an electronic leak detector (Fig. 2-31) will detect even the most minute leak without the need for disturbing or removing components. The *Hallide* unit utilizes a flame which is played over the suspected component. If the flame turns a different color, a leak is indicated, the size of the leak being estimated by the color of the flame. Small leaks turn the flame green, larger leaks turn it purple. When a leak is encountered, the electronic detector either buzzes or causes a meter deflection.

If a leak test must be made and no leak detection instrument is available, the system must first be purged and the compressor taken out of the system. Valves are attached to the open tubing and the system subjected to pressures in excess of 50 psi. Many servicemen prefer using *Refrigerant-11* for this purpose, because it is easy to handle and has a boiling point at

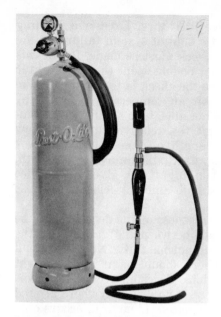

Fig. 2-30. *Hallide* leak detector.

Courtesy Linde Co. Div., Union Carbide Corp.

Courtesy General Electric Co.

Fig. 2-31. Electronic leak detector.

approximately room temperature. *R-11* is also useful to flush out a system since it remains in a liquid state throughout the refrigerant cycle, and can therefore wash out any dirt particles that may have accumulated

Once a system is opened, most servicemen prefer to install new restrictor tubing rather than risk the old one having an obstruction. It is also mandatory that a new dryer/strainer be installed whenever a system is opened.

Unit analysis—If any of the following conditions is the only one encountered in servicing the refrigerator or freezer, the compressor *need not* be replaced:

a. High-side leak resulting in partial or complete loss of refrigerant charge.
b. Low-side leaks in the components located *outside* the refrigerated space.
c. Too much refrigerant charge (a rare condition, unless the system has been opened since manufacture).
d. Too little refrigerant charge.
e. The presence of moisture in the system as a result of low-side leaks in the components located *outside* the refrigerated space.
f. Moisture in the line due to high-side leaks.

Replacement of the compressor is *always* indicated under any of the following conditions:

a. Broken tubing (provided the unit has been operating with the broken tubing. If the unit has never been operated, however, no compressor replacement is necessary).
b. Any leak detected in the low side of the system in any component located *within* the refrigerated space.
c. Particles of burned-out motor windings detected in any part of the system. Another test for motor burnout employs a chemical paper similar to litmus on which a few drops of the system refrigerant are allowed to fall. If the paper turns a different color, a motor burnout has occurred.
d. Oil and refrigerant leaks at the compressor terminals, housing welds, or tubing joints at or near the compressor.
e. Noisy or stuck compressor, or a compressor that runs without pumping.

Electrical Tests

The following electrical tests are designed to tell the serviceman whether or not a particular component is open, or shorted,

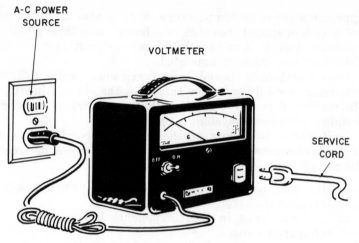

A-C POWER
SOURCE

VOLTMETER

SERVICE
CORD

Fig. 2-32. Line voltage check.

and whether it requires repair or replacement. It also gives him other information of value in diagnosing the cause of a failure.

Line Voltage—Plug the refrigerator or freezer service cord into the voltmeter and plug the voltmeter into the power source (Fig. 2-32). Line voltage should be read with the refrigerator running under normal load at the time of the test. Other appliances in the home which would normally operate at the same time should also be turned on.

Switch terminals—Place a test lamp across the various contacts in the switch (Fig. 2-33). If the lamp fails to light, a defective switch is indicated.

Relay test—Excessive consumption of power by the compressor on reaching run speed could indicate a relay that is not dropping out of the circuit properly after start. Low line voltage will sometimes cause the relay to "chatter." To check this, short out the relay with a jumper wire across the proper terminals (refer to the manufacturer's literature to determine which terminals to jump). Apply the short during compressor run for no more than 2 or 3 seconds at a time. If the compressor runs properly during the test, a faulty relay is indicated.

Overload test—Use a wattmeter and a jumper wire to check the overload protector. The jumper should be connected be-

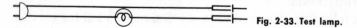

Fig. 2-33. Test lamp.

tween the screw terminal on the overload protector and the common terminal on the compressor. Turn the unit on; if the compressor does not start, but the wattmeter indicates a higher than normal reading, the protector is probably good. If the compressor starts, and the wattmeter reading is normal, the protector should be replaced.

Capacitor test—The easiest test for a defective capacitor is to replace it with one known to be good. Be sure to replace it with a capacitor of exactly the same microfarad rating. A capacitor can also be tested by making a resistance check, but it must first be discharged by pulling the power plug from the wall outlet and shorting across the capacitor terminals with a jumper wire. Set an ohmmeter on the 1-megohm scale, take a reading across the capacitor, and then discharge it again. Now, reverse the leads and take another reading.. If the ohmmeter needle stabilizes at 30,000 ohms or less, the capacitor should be considered leaky and replaced. If the needle does not move at all, the capacitor is open.

Compressor test—Pull the service cord from the wall outlet and disconnect and insulate all the relay leads. Remove the terminal cover from the compressor housing and connect a test cord to the common (C) and run (R) terminals. These terminals may be numbered on some compressors as follows: Start terminal (No. 1), common terminal (No. 2), and run terminal (No. 3).

Attach one end of a jumper wire to the start (S) terminal. Plug the test cord into a wall outlet and momentarily touch the other end of the jumper wire to the run (R) terminal. If the motor begins to run, there is nothing wrong in the motor windings.

It is important in making this test to apply current only for a few seconds at a time, since none of the motor's protective devices are in use.

Wiring test—Check for broken wires by visual inspection as far as possible, or by placing a test cord between various components in turn until the open is isolated.

Solenoid test (two-temperature models and convertibles)— With this unit operating in normal refrigeration cycle, place a test lamp across the terminals of the initiator mechanism (counter cam, defrost-cycle timer, or hand switch). If the lamp fails to glow, the solenoid coil is shorted (provided the wiring harness is unbroken).

Ohmmeter test—In place of a jumper wire or test lamp, some servicemen prefer to use an ohmmeter. An ohmmeter will detect leaky or intermittent conditions not usually detectable by other methods. Follow the preceding steps under "Capacitor test." *Never use an ohmmeter with the power to the refrigerator on.*

Hook-on ammeter—This is a useful device because it does not require component disassembly for amperage readings. The instrument is closed around a wire and readings taken directly from a dial. Be sure that all normal load conditions are in existence at the time of the test.

Wattmeter test—A great deal can be learned about the performance of a compressor by taking wattage readings under different conditions. The wattage consumption of a refrigeration system will vary with ambient temperature and the pressure within the system. To test accurately, the serviceman must compare the wattage readings against specific evaporator temperatures given in manufacturer's service literature.

Power consumption of a typical refrigerator/freezer combination is given in Table 2-2. Readings are taken by connecting a wattmeter directly to the compressor terminals by means of a test cord. If the test cord is not used, an additional 50 watts or so should be added to the typical wattage figures to compensate for the wattage consumed by other components in the circuit.

To get an accurate temperature reading at the evaporator, the thermometer tip should be frozen to the bottom center of the evaporator unit.

Table 2-2. Wattage Consumption Data of a Typical 1/5 hp Motor Compressor

at plus 10°F		at 0°F		at minus 10°F	
Min.	Max.	Min.	Max.	Min.	Max.
220	256	197	233	177	213

Readings taken with compressor in operation

COMMON REFRIGERATOR AND FREEZER REPAIRS

To keep failures to a minimum, the customer should be cautioned on the following points:

1. The number and lengths of time a refrigerator or freezer door is opened will greatly add to the accumulation of frost on the evaporator. A table placed on the door-handle side and adjacent to the refrigerator will cut down on frost accumulation by reducing the number of trips to

the refrigerator from the sink, etc., and by eliminating the tendency to leave the door open between trips.

2. Those models without automatic defrosting should be defrosted regularly—about twice as frequently in hot as in cold weather. Frost should never be permitted to build up to a thick coating on the evaporator, because this reduces heat transfer and impairs the efficiency of the unit. Frost also traps and holds food odors.

3. Clean the condenser (if of the exposed type) regularly with a long bristle brush on the end of a vacuum cleaner tube. Dirt on the condenser clogs the natural draft of air and drastically cuts refrigerating efficiency.

Recharging

There are several ways in which a refrigeration system may be recharged with refrigerant. Following are the basic considerations in recharging.

Clean the suction line with steel wool in an area 4 to 6 inches from the compressor housing joint. Crimp the suction line and nick it slightly with a file to bleed off the refrigerant charge. Be careful that no open flames are nearby when this is done, as harmful compounds may form.

When all the pressure has been bled off, cut out a portion of the suction line above and below the nick with a tube cutter, leaving a gap long enough to accommodate the tubing tee which will be installed later. Connect a portable charging stand (Fig. 2-34) to the compressor tube stub by means of a compression or flare fitting. The charging stand consists of a measuring refrigerant cylinder marked with a scale to measure the charge in ounces, and a compound gauge marked in pounds per square inch (psig) above atmospheric pressure and inches of mercury vacuum below atmospheric pressure. The refrigerant measuring cylinder is connected to a refrigerant-supply cylinder. Be sure to purge all lines and connections in the manner prescribed by the equipment manufacturer.

A pressure gauge, marked in psig, a hand valve, and a length of purging hose are connected in series to the other end of the suction tube.

If the compressor is to remain in the system (no replacement required), a further check can be made at this point to determine compressor efficiency. Open the hand valve in the purging line and start the motor compressor. Reading the compound gauge, check to see that the compressor evacuates the system to 26 inches of mercury vacuum within 5 minutes. (Figures are at sea level—to correct for other altitudes, sub-

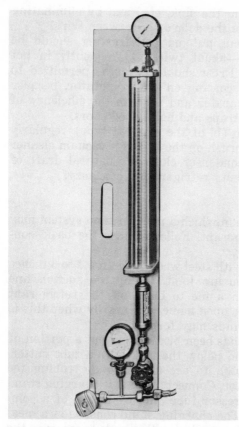

Fig. 2-34. Portable charging stand.

tract ½ inch of mercury vacuum for each 1,000 feet above sea level.)

Another test that can be made at this time is the action of the discharge valve in the compressor. Close the purging-hose hand valve, and admit at least 25 psig into the system through the measuring cylinder. Now, run the compressor until the compound gauge on the suction side reads 20 or more inches of mercury vacuum. Shut off the compressor. If the gauge readings do not change, the discharge valve inside the compressor is seated properly. If the needle on the compound gauge returns toward the zero reading immediately and the pressure on the pressure gauge drops, it means that the valve is permitting refrigerant vapor to seep back into the compressor, and the unit must be replaced.

If it is necessary to disconnect the charging equipment at this point, wait until the pressure on the suction side builds up at least 5 psig before disconnecting the lines. This prevents air from entering the system.

To charge the system (Fig. 2-35) disconnect the foregoing apparatus and solder a tee in the suction line where it has been cut. Also install a tee in the discharge line at about the same distance from the compressor.

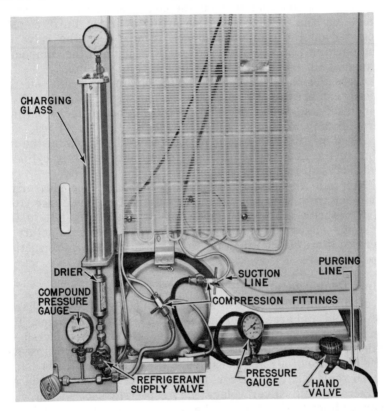

Fig. 2-35. Charging a system.

Remove the production dryer and install a new dryer strainer combination in its place, following instructions contained on the package. Do not break the seal of the new unit until just before installation, to prevent airborne moisture from saturating the drying agent.

Reconnect the charging stand and compound gauge to the free end of the suction tee, using a compression or flare fitting. Connect a pressure gauge, hand valve, and purging hose in series and fasten them to the open end of the discharge tee.

Pressurize the system and check for leaks. Small leaks at joints may be repaired by reheating the joint, adding solder if necessary.

Open the hand valve in the purging line and start the compressor. Continue until 26 inches of mercury vacuum are registered on the compound gauge. Close the hand valve in the purging line and shut off the compressor. Open the hand valve on the refrigerant measuring cylinder until 5 psig register on the compound gauge. Again, open the valve on the purging line and start the compressor until the compound gauge again reaches 26 inches of mercury vacuum.

Close the hand valve in the purging line and shut off the motor compressor. Pressure the system again to 5 psig. Now pinch off and solder the end of the discharge tee. Continue pressurizing to 50 psig and leak test the pinched-off tee.

Bleed off the refrigerant in the system by cracking the fitting in the hand valve of the refrigerant measuring cylinder until pressure drops to 5 psig.

Now add the proper refrigerant charge to the measuring cylinder from the supply cylinder, subtracting one ounce from the prescribed charge to make up for the 5 psig left in the system. (Prescribed charges are found in manufacturer's service literature.) Pinch off, solder, and leak test the suction tee end.

Unit Replacement

Replacement compressors are supplied with a full charge of oil and a charge of refrigerant vapor or dry nitrogen. The ends of the suction and discharge tubing are soldered or plugged to maintain pressure during shipment and to prevent the entrance of air and moisture to the interior of the housing.

To replace a compressor, position it on the base of the refrigerator and silver solder the respective suction and discharge lines to the stubs on the replacement compressor. Stubs are usually marked for identification. Follow charging procedure as outlined.

Soldering Copper Tubing

Copper tubing is used in refrigeration systems because it resists the corrosive effects of the refrigerant, and because it bends easily without kinking. It is also convenient to use because it may be easily joined in pressure tight joints.

To solder a tube to a fitting, clean the areas to be joined thoroughly with steel wool. Apply soldering paste to all surfaces to be joined. Fit the pieces firmly together and heat with a blowtorch for a few seconds. Now apply the tip of a length of solder to the point where the tubing enters the fitting. Capillary action, and the action of heat will cause the liquefied solder to run deeply into the joint, where it solidifies and forms a gas-tight seal.

Unsweating a joint involves heating it until the solder liquefies, then pulling tubing and fitting apart.

TROUBLESHOOTING GUIDE

The following "symptoms" are the signs of trouble in the system. Each symptom is followed by a number of possible causes and remedies. The list is by no means complete,, but it will serve as a guide to the more common failures and causes of failure in a refrigerator or freezer system.

Unit Will Not Operate, No Interior Light

1. Power cord removed from or loose in wall outlet.
2. Blown fuse. Check line voltage at outlet. Voltage should be no more than 10% higher or lower than normal. Check for an excessive number of appliances working off the same branch line. Replace fuse.

Unit Will Not Operate, Interior Light On

1. Defective switches. Test switches as outlined previously.
2. Defective thermostat. Test as outlined previously.
3. Defective relay. Test as outlined previously.
4. Defective overload protector. Test as outlined previously.
5. Defective capacitor. Replace.
6. Open or shorted compressor. Test as outlined previously.
7. Broken lead wires. Visual inspection or test as outlined previously.

No Defrosting Cycle

1. Initiator mechanism defective. Test by visual inspection or with test lamp across wiring terminals. Manually rotate cam to test for free movement.
2. Open or shorted solenoid valve coil. With the solenoid control in the position which normally supplies current to the valve, test across wiring terminals.

Unit Runs Continuously, Cabinet Warm

1. Extreme hot weather conditions may contribute to symptom.
2. Poor door seal at gasket.

3. Interior light may stay on when door is closed. Check door light switch.

Unit Runs Continuously, Cabinet Cold

1. Defective thermostat.

Defrost Water Not Evaporating

1. If defrost vaporizer coil is employed, check across terminals with test lamp.
2. Condenser fan defective. Check fan motor with test lamp.

Noisy Operation

1. Check for misaligned fan blades, loose tubing connections, (particularly around motor compressor), defective fan motor bearings, or loose compressor mountings.
2. If noise seems to come from within the compressor and does not stop after the unit has been in operation for a short time, internal trouble is indicated, such as broken internal mountings, loose shaft bearings, or worn piston rings. Compressor should be given compression test or replaced.
3. If the noise is a loud click at start, it indicates that the motor overload protector is operating. This is not a bad sign in itself, but it is an indication that an overload condition is being encountered. If condition persists, make a unit analysis.
4. High head pressure may cause noisy operation of the compressor. Check for extremely clogged condition around condenser fins.

CHAPTER 3

WASHING MACHINES

Years ago, by a mountain stream in Zamboanga, the author watched a group of women washing clothes. The method used was the one that had been used for centuries—the item of clothing, soaking wet, was laid on a partially immersed flat rock and pounded repeatedly with a flat, wooden paddle. While this universally used technique may appear to be crude and inefficient, no one who has visited in the Pacific can fail to notice the brilliance of the white and colored clothes worn by the natives—all washed by hand and without benefit of modern detergents.

While such washing methods are not practical for our automated society, all the elements of an efficient washday technique are there. Torrents of water soften the fibers of the clothing and loosen foreign particles (soak or preliminary rinse). A period of pounding follows (agitation and wash cycle). After the pounding, the clothes are dumped into a weighted wicker basket immersed in the flowing stream of water (final clear rinse). If just one more cycle is added, the spin dry cycle, the essential functions of a modern washing machine are outlined.

Modern washers can be divided roughly into two main groups—the automatic type (further subdivided into tumbler and agitator), and the conventional type (subdivided into wringer and twin-tub washers).

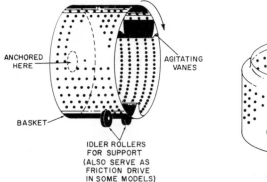

Fig. 3-1. Cylinder basket of tumbler washer.

Fig. 3-2. Agitator washer cylinder basket.

TUMBLER WASHERS

Most tumbler washers are "front loading," meaning that the clothes are placed in the washer through a door that opens to the front. A few tumbler washers have borrowed a page out of the commercial laundry book and provided a door on the circumference of the cylinder basket through which the clothes are loaded or removed.

The cylindrical basket of a tumbler washer rotates in a horizontal plane—that is, its axis is parallel to the floor (Fig. 3-1). In some models the axis is inclined slightly, sloping to the rear. Agitation of the clothes occurs by lifting them out of the soapy water by means of the rotating basket, and letting them fall back into the water of their own weight as they reach the top of the revolution.

The cylinder basket revolves slowly (about 50 rpm) during the wash and rinse periods, at the end of which the water is drained from the machine. The cylinder basket then revolves much faster (600 rpm for "normal action," 300 rpm for "gentle action") to spin the clothes damp dry and ready for final drying.

Because there is no agitator in a tumbler washer, construction tends to be somewhat simpler, requiring only a means to spin the cylinder basket at two (or three) different speeds.

64

AGITATOR WASHERS

Agitator washers are loaded from the top. In this type the axis of the cylinder basket is vertical to the floor (Fig. 3-2), and the basket does not spin during the wash or agitation cycle. Instead, an agitator oscillates in the tub, sloshing the water and the clothes through an arc of about 180°. Some agitators have a vertical motion as well, and still others incline the plane of movement from the vertical, causing an undulating motion. These additional motions are designed to create greater turbulence in the water for maximum loosening of dirt.

AUTOMATIC WASHER

An automatic washing machine is probably the most complicated piece of machinery in the modern home (see pictorial diagram, Fig. 3-3). It is complicated because it is required to perform a great many functions in the course of the complete washing cycle.

First, the customer selects the desired temperature of the water to be used and the amount needed for varying loads. The maximum load of clothes should average from 8 to 10 lbs. dry weight, although some manufacturers claim greater capacity for their washers. A detergent (and bleach, softeners, etc., if desired) is added to the proper receptacle or placed

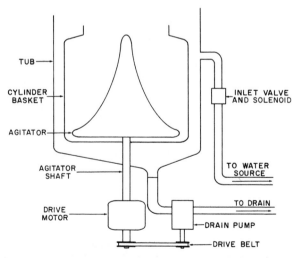

Fig. 3-3. Pictorial diagram, automatic washer.

directly into the machine. Then a button is pushed or a dial is turned, causing the machine to take over and begin the washing.

The act of turning on the machine actually does no more than close circuits to the drive and timer motors. The drive motor in most machines is coupled to (1) the agitator or, in tumbler washers, the cylinder basket, and (2) a water pump. A secondary circuit in the electrical system feeds current to a timer motor which controls all the operations of the machine during the entire wash and spin cycles.

Fig. 3-4. Control panel, automatic washer.

When the customer turns the various selector dials (Fig. 3-4) for the type of washing desired, a set of cams is aligned, presetting a switch and adjusting a pair of water-inlet valves. If the machine offers a choice of either normal or gentle action, a different set of cam wheels is brought into play for the selection made. These cam wheels are revolved slowly by the timer motor. As they revolve, their surfaces make contact with switches at various points in their travel, opening and closing circuits to energize solenoids, and segments of circuits to activate or stop the various components in the system.

Most machines offer a choice of fill levels—high, medium, or low—depending on the amount of wash to be done. When the customer makes a fill selection, a pressure switch (Fig. 3-5) or a float switch is in reality being preset to open when the proper level is reached. In the same manner, selecting hot, warm, or cold wash water involves opening or closing the water inlet valves by means of solenoids.

The fill switch in most machines is in control throughout the operation, except that it is bypassed at the Empty position during the brief spray rinses. With the fill switch in control, the agitator cannot function until the machine is filled with water to the proper level. Initially, then, when the customer pushes the start button, the water-pump inlet valve is opened and water is admitted into the machine. If the customer had selected a hot wash cycle, a solenoid is energized to open the hot water inlet, by-passing the cold water solenoid valve, or vice versa for a cold wash. If a warm wash had been selected, both solenoids would be energized. The water is cut off by the pressure or float switch when the proper level is reached.

In the meantime, the timer motor has been slowly revolving, rotating the cam wheels until finally a switch closes that completes the circuit to the transmission. The fill switch is still in control, however, and will not permit current to flow to energize the transmission until fill has been achieved.

When the fill switch has been satisfied, current to the transmission now flows and another solenoid is energized. This solenoid, through mechanical means which will be examined later, causes the drive clutch to engage and the agitator begins to oscillate, or the tumbler basket begins to revolve in the wash cycle.

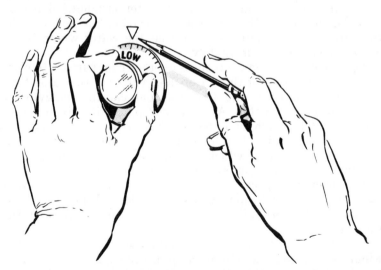

Fig. 3-5. Pressure switch controls fill.

Agitators as well as the cylinder basket in tumbler washers are driven through either a gear train or a clutch arrangement. In the case of an agitator, it is driven either by means of (1) a train consisting of a pinion gear, a drive gear, a connecting rod, and a sector gear, or (2) a rack and pinion arrangement. These mechanical assemblies serve to convert the rotary motion of the drive motor to an oscillating motion, driving the agitator through an arc of about 180° at 60 strokes per minute. In some agitator washers, the cylinder basket may wobble slightly during agitation, but it does not spin. However, during the spin cycle, the agitator is locked in with the cylinder basket so that both are turning. If the agitator did not turn during spin, the clothes would be in danger of being torn between the spinning basket and the stationary agitator.

After the agitation or wash cycle, a cam surface on the timer-motor cam assembly closes another switch, energizing a solenoid valve to open and drain the tub. In most washers, the water pump is constantly in operation during the entire wash and spin cycle so that it is only necessary to open and close various valves in the water system to achieve fill, drain, and spray rinses. During drain, all motion of the agitator or cylinder basket stops under the control of the fill switch, which will not permit resumption of drive until all the water is emptied from the tub.

A short spin cycle may follow, designed to remove any suds that may remain in the tub and the clothes. A spray rinse, in which a small amount of water is admitted briefly into the tub, helps this cycle along. During the spray cycle, the outlet valve remains open so that the water which is admitted drains out immediately.

The timer motor now advances another cam surface to close the switch controlling the water-inlet valve, at the same time opening the circuit to the drive solenoid, causing the cylinder basket to come to a stop. After a brief pause, the timer motor closes the fill switch and the tub fills with water again. In some washers, this fill temperature may be pre-selected at the start from a dial which affords various combinations of hot, warm or cold wash, and warm or cold rinses.

The deep-rinsing cycle is usually brief, accompanied by a short period of agitation. At its conclusion, all motion of the cylinder basket or agitator again comes to a stop and the tub empties.

The washer now goes into the final rinse and spin-dry cycles. Final rinsing may consist of a spin, accompanied by one or two brief spray rinses, the purpose of which is to dislodge, through the holes in the cylinder basket, any residue of soap scum or dirt which may have been deposited on the surface of the clothes as the water level receded during the drain cycle. After the last spray rinse, the cylinder basket continues to spin at high speed for a few minutes, during which most of the water is driven out of the clothes by the centrifugal force of the spin.

Finally, the timer motor advances to a point where all circuits are opened and the washer shuts itself off.

CONVENTIONAL WASHERS

Conventional washers are relatively simple in operation (Fig. 3-7). The user fills the tub by means of a hose connected to a nearby mixing faucet, soap and bleach are added, and the washer motor is turned on. The customer starts agitation by throwing a clutch lever which engages a gear train similar to that used in an automatic washer. The agitator operates with an oscillating motion until the customer decides the clothes have been washed long enough. The agitator clutch lever is then disengaged and the hand-operated drain valve turned to Drain.

It is important to understand the need for the agitator to stop during drain. If it were to continue operating without water in the tub, it would be many times more difficult to push against the weight of the clothes, probably causing a motor

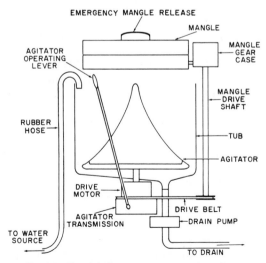

Fig. 3-7. Pictorial diagram, conventional washer.

overload. In addition, the clothes themselves might become mangled in the process.

Draining is accomplished in a conventional washer either by gravity (permitting the water to flow down through the drain hose into a drain in the floor of the laundry room), or by means of a water pump. The pump operates continuously as long as the motor is turned on, the customer accomplishing draining by opening a valve in the pump. The tub is then re-filled with clear water for a deep rinse, also accompanied by agitation.

In a wringer washer the mangle is turned on by means of a lever. This engages a vertical shaft which transfers power from the drive motor to the mangle gear train and rollers. The rollers of the mangle are made of soft rubber or composition

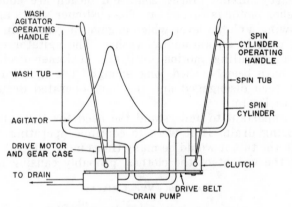

Fig. 3-8. Pictorial diagram, twin-tub washer.

and are adjustable by means of a pressure-regulating knob. A safety feature found on most machines springs the entire mangle assembly open if a bulky object is introduced between the rollers.

In twin-tub conventional washers (Fig. 3-8), the customer places the damp clothes in a spin basket, which is caused to rotate at high speed by engaging another clutch lever. Most twin-tub washers, however, have a basket of relatively small diameter, necessitating a much higher rate of spin than the large diameter basket of an automatic washer. Some of the older models of twin-tub washers have no safety switch to stop the spin basket when the access door is opened. All later models do have some such device, as well as a braking mechanism to bring the spinning basket to a stop as quickly as possible.

70

WASHER COMPONENTS

In order to service a washing machine, it is important to understand the functioning of each of its components, as well as the functioning of the machine as a whole. Since there are many different makes and models of washers on the market, it would not be possible to describe each and every one in a book of this scope. However, most washers operate on the same general principles, employing components which, in their most important aspects, resemble each other enough so that a general discussion and description of one will result in sufficient knowledge to check the performance and functioning of other makes and types.

No detailed discussion of conventional washer components will be given where the component is similar to that found in an automatic, such as the agitator gear train and the water pump.

Washing machines are composed of three major assemblies—the mechanical system, the electrical system, and the water system.

MECHANICAL SYSTEM

In this group of components are found the main-drive motor, the gear-train assembly which powers the agitator in agitator washers, and the basket-drive and brake assembly which drives the basket in both agitator and tumbler washers.

Gear Train

As mentioned previously, gear trains in agitator washers may be either of the sector gear, connector rod, or the rack and pinion gear type.

In the rack and pinion type (Fig. 3-10), a pinion gear is driven by the main belt, taking power from the motor by means of a system of pulleys. The pinion gear drives a larger-diameter main-drive gear. Through a variation of the sizes of the pinion-gear pulley, the pinion gear, and the main-drive gear, a speed reduction is effected so that the main-drive gear revolves at about 120 rpm. The main-drive gear is usually mounted on an eccentric stud to permit adjustment of the gear mesh for quiet operation.

A stud mounted on the main-drive provides a bearing surface for a connecting rod, which is machined at its other end with a row of gear teeth, called a *rack*. As the main-drive gear rotates, the connecting rod is moved back and forth at

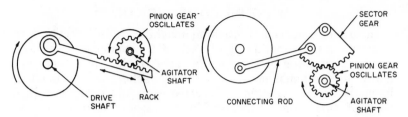

Fig. 3-10. Rack and pinion drive.   Fig. 3-11. Sector gear drive.

about 60 complete strokes per minute. The rack end of the connecting rod meshes with the teeth on the agitator gear, imparting an oscillating motion to the agitator, which travels approximately 180°, first in one direction, then the other, also at approximately 60 complete movements per minute.

In a variation of this method, a sector gear (Fig. 3-11) is employed in place of the rack gear. A pinion gear drives a larger main-drive gear as in the previous example. A connecting rod is attached, through bearing surfaces on both ends, to the main-drive gear and a sector gear, the latter pivoting on a stud through a 180° arc. The sector gear meshes with the agitator gear to accomplish oscillation.

In both methods the drive belt is operating continuously as long as the motor is turned on, which means that the agitator would oscillate continuously if some method were not introduced to disengage the gear train at the appropriate points in the washing cycle. This is accomplished by translating the electrical impulse furnished to a solenoid plunger into mechanical action.

It is important to understand that the amount of force exerted by a solenoid plunger would never, of itself, be sufficient to disengage the gear train of a mechanical system powered by a ⅓ or ½ hp motor. Some other means of actually extracting a gear from the train must be used. Thus, the extraction is initiated but not actually accomplished by the solenoid plunger. Here's how one such system works:

The location chosen for the breaking of the gear train is the meeting of the rack or sector gear with the agitator shaft. This provides the greatest amount of cushioning for the sudden shock of the meshing of the gear tooth.

The agitator gear may be moved to one of two positions on the agitator shaft (Fig. 3-12). In its upper position it locks with the shaft by means of a pin. A spring exerts pressure downward, keeping the gear from locking with the agitator shaft. In its lower position, the agitator gear oscillates freely, entirely independent of the agitator.

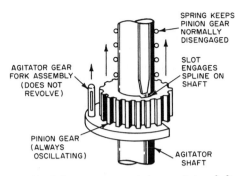

Fig._3-12. Agitator gear mounted on agitator shaft.

A solenoid assembly is mounted on the shaft of the sector gear (Fig. 3-13) or connecting rod rack so that the entire solenoid assembly rocks back and forth with it. A cam bar is mounted between the solenoid assembly and the agitator gear. The plunger of the solenoid normally stays down of its own weight. The lower end of the plunger is slotted so that the plunger straddles the cam bar, and a horizontal pin is fitted to the ends of the fork formed by the slot in the plunger, passing through a two-level slot in the cam bar (Fig. 3-14). Normally, the plunger rides in the lower level of the slot, carried there by its own weight.

The lower slot on the cam bar is so located that the rocking (lateral) action of the solenoid assembly riding on the sector gear will maintain the cam bar in the withdrawn, or back position, of its lateral travel.

As soon as the solenoid is energized, however, it pulls the plunger upward. On the next rocking motion the plunger is pulled up into the upper level of the cam-bar slot (Fig. 3-15). This slot is so located that the rocking action (powered by

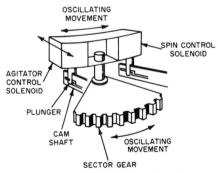

Fig. 3-13. Solenoid assembly rides on the sector gear shaft.

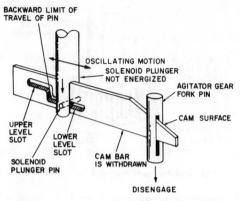

Fig. 3-14. Solenoid plunger detail, not actuated.

the drive motor, not by the solenoid coil) will push the cam bar forward. A cam surface at the agitator gear end of the cam bar causes the agitator gear fork to travel upward, taking the agitator gear with it. The latter now engages with the pin in the agitator drive shaft, and the agitator begins to oscillate.

When the solenoid circuit is opened, the plunger will fall of its own weight, dropping to the lower level of the slot on

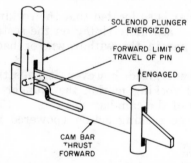

Fig. 3-15. Solenoid plunger energized.

the cam bar and thus withdrawing the front end of the cam bar from the agitator fork. This permits the spring on the agitator shaft to force the agitator gear downward to disengage it.

Basket Drive and Brake Assembly

In both agitator- and tumbler-type washers, the cylinder basket is driven by a V-belt riding on a drive pulley. In agitator washers the same belt drives both the basket and pinion gear pulleys.

In tumbler washers it is necessary to reduce the speed of the cylinder basket from approximately 600 rpm in the spin cycle to the 50 or 60 rpm required in the wash cycle. This is accomplished by a transmission or speed-change unit actuated by a solenoid plunger in much the same manner as described in the section on the agitator gear train.

A cylinder basket loaded with wet clothes and spinning at 600 rpm develops many hundreds of pounds of inertial force. This force is not only dangerous, but tends to keep the cylinder basket spinning for a very long time after the driving force is removed. Some sort of braking system is therefore required, for reasons of both safety and efficiency.

A typical basket drive and brake assembly for an agitator washer is pictured in Fig. 3-16. For this type washer the agitator shaft passes through a drive tube, on which the cylinder basket is force-fitted. When the drive tube rotates, the cylinder basket rotates with it. The agitator shaft and the drive tube rotate independently of each other except during spin, when they are locked together as previously noted.

The basket-drive pulley is always turning whenever the drive motor is operating; it revolves freely on the drive tube. Directly above the basket-drive pulley is a basket-drive clutch disc which is permanently attached to the drive tube and is positioned to narrowly miss contact with a special clutch lining mounted on the top of the basket-drive pulley. Above the clutch disc is mounted the stationary brake yoke. A tension spring tends to pull the brake yoke downward, exerting pressure against the clutch disc tending to cause it to engage the clutch lining on the basket drive pulley. This engagement is prevented, however, by a basket clutch shaft riding on the

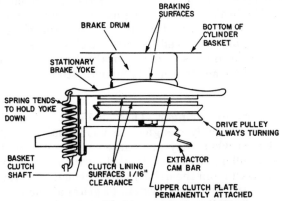

Fig. 3-16. Basket drive and brake assembly.

top edge of an extractor cam bar, which is normally thrust forward into a slot in the clutch shaft.

Above the brake yoke is mounted a brake-drum assembly, which is normally pressed against brake linings on both the bottom of the tub and the top of the brake yoke.

A solenoid assembly is mounted on the pivot stud of the sector gear, exactly the same as in the previous gear train discussion. As long as the solenoid is not energized, the plunger pin rides in the lower level of the extractor cam bar, allowing it to remain thrust forward into and holding up the basket clutch shaft.

When the solenoid is energized, the plunger is pulled upward by the magnetic force of the coil and the pin now rides back and forth in the upper slot of the extractor cam bar. In so doing, it pulls the extractor cam bar backward out of the slot in the basket clutch shaft, allowing the latter to slide downward on the inclined cam surface of the bar toward the clutch lining.

The tension spring now forces the brake yoke downward, pressing the basket-drive clutch disc against the clutch lining on the top of the basket drive pulley. After an initial slippage, the clutch lining firmly engages the basket drive clutch disc (permanently attached to the basket-drive tube) and the cylinder basket begins to rotate. The basket gradually builds up speed until there is no longer any slippage and the full speed and power of the motor is transmitted to the basket for the duration of the spin cycle.

When the solenoid is de-energized (either by opening the loading door or at the end of the spin cycle) the plunger drops down into the lower-level slot of the extractor cam bar. This pushes the front end of the bar into the basket clutch shaft and forces the brake yoke upward against the force of the tension spring to disengage the clutch from the clutch lining. As the brake yoke is forced upward, it closes the distance between the brake drums and the brake linings, bringing the heavily loaded basket to a quick, smooth stop.

Mangle

The mangle, or wringer, (Fig. 3-17) of a conventional washer is an assembly designed to wring out moisture from the wet clothes when they are passed between two rubber or composition rollers under controlled pressure. Power for the wringer is taken from the drive motor through a wringer-drive shaft (Fig. 3-18) turning a system of gears at the lower roller. The upper roller idles in most machines. A lever engages the

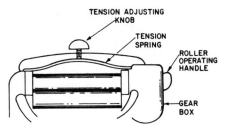

Fig. 3-17. Mangle of wringer washer.

gear train to operate the rollers, and generally affords three positions—forward, reverse, and stop.

A safety device to relieve the pressure on the rollers is usually provided. In some models, this device is automatic, springing open the entire mechanism when a bulky, unyielding object attempts to pass through the rollers. In others, a large button

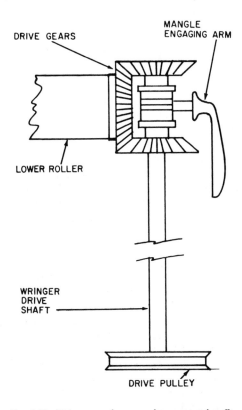

Fig. 3-18. Wringer washer mangle power take-off.

or bar on the top of the assembly must be struck to relieve the pressure. In either case, resetting the rollers is simply a matter of depressing the upper roller housing until it locks.

Mangle assemblies are designed to pivot on the wringer drive shaft housing so that the entire assembly may be swung out of the way during the washing cycle, if desired.

Cabinet Components

The cabinet, besides serving the function of enclosing the washer in an attractive case, also serves to house, anchor, and separate the components. In nearly all washers, whether of the tumbler, agitator, or conventional type, the moving parts are found in a compartment at the bottom of the cabinet, separated from the other components by the bottom of the tub. In tumbler washers, the motor is mounted with its axis parallel to the floor, the drive belt to the cylinder basket pulley being at the rear of the machine. In agitator washers and in the conventional types, the motor is mounted with its axis at right angles to the floor, the belt pulleys traveling in a horizontal plane.

Agitators—Most agitators used in today's washing machines are of molded plastic, while those in earlier units were made of cast aluminum. Some have relatively straight vanes with a slight sweep, similar to a triangular sail before a breeze. Others have undulating shapes which cause the clothes to rise and fall as well as oscillate horizontally. Extra precautions are taken by the manufacturers to insure a positive lock between the agitator and its shaft. In some, a press-fitted locking lug of a shape to fit into a hexagonal tapered hole in the agitator body provides a firm seating for the agitator to prevent whipping. Removal of this lug, sometimes required for access to the gear case and other mechanical components, necessitates the use of a special lug-puller tool.

Not all washing machines employ the type of agitator that oscillates through an arc. One popular make causes the agitator to move up and down in a fast pumping motion, instead of turning. Still another moves the agitator in a slow, off-center movement that does not turn on itself.

Cylinder Basket (Figs. 3-1 and 3-2)—The cylinder basket of most washers is made of porcelain enameled steel. Holes in the sides and bottom permit the free passage of water in and out, even when loaded with clothes. The basket of an agitator washer, being positioned upright, usually has a conical-shaped bottom so that no dirt or residue is trapped and to insure complete drainage.

A tumbler washer basket usually is fitted with baffles placed at right angles to the circumference to help carry the clothes to the top as the basket revolves. The clothes then drop of their own weight into the water. Baffles also help create more turbulence to loosen dirt more efficiently.

Tub—Both the tumbler- and agitator-type washers require an outer tub to contain the water through which the cylinder basket revolves. Outer tubs are also generally made of porcelain enameled steel and are provided with holes fitted with seals and sleeves for fastening the various hose connections. A large drain hole in the bottom of the tub may be provided with a baffle to prevent the air lock that sometimes occurs

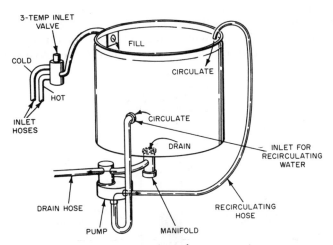

Fig. 3-19. Automatic washer water system.

when swirling water attempts to pass down a drain. Other baffles may be positioned at strategic places on the tub bottom to increase turbulence.

Base Plate—The mechanical units of the washer are mounted on a heavy-gauge steel base plate. In agitator washers, the base plate also supports a heavy central flange on which is pressed the tube that houses the agitator shaft and the basket drive tube.

THE WATER SYSTEM

The water system in an automatic washer (Fig. 3-19) consists of a series of valves, a water pump, and various accessory components such as dispensers, filters, hoses, etc.

Water enters the tub through an inlet valve, which may or may not provide an automatic temperature control for mixing hot and cold water. Usually, water enters the machine due to its own pressure. As the water level rises, it actuates the fill switch, closing the circuit to the agitator control solenoid and the machine begins the wash cycle.

In some machines, the water pump also serves to recirculate the water, taking it from the bottom of the tub and forcing it out through an inlet above the water level near the top of the tub. This recirculation serves to insure that soaps and bleach are thoroughly mixed with the wash water. Energizing a solenoid on the water pump permits the passage of the recirculated water driven by the recirculating impeller.

Water is ejected from the tub by the discharge impeller of the water pump. Discharge is effected by flapper valves in the body of the pump, which are actuated by the same mechanism that motivates the gear extraction in the drive system.

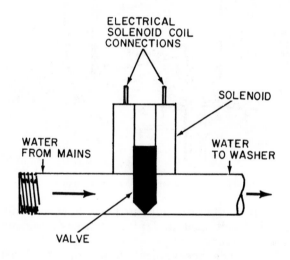

Fig. 3-20. Solenoid off-on valve.

Valves

The inlet valves of an automatic washer are operated by solenoid coils and plungers to permit or obstruct the passage of water. There are three basic types.

Single solenoid shut-off valve (Fig. 3-20)—In this type, the solenoid performs only the function of shut-off, the mixing of incoming hot and cold water for desired wash and rinse temperature being performed at the faucets by the user.

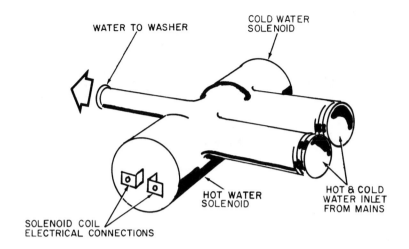

Fig. 3-21. Double-solenoid shut-off valve.

Double solenoid shut-off valve (Fig. 3-21)—This type of valve permits three water temperature selections—hot, warm, and cold. Energizing of the cold-water solenoid permits only the passage of cold water; energizing the hot-water solenoid allows only hot water to enter. When both solenoids are energized, both hot and cold water are admitted to the tub, resulting in a warm wash.

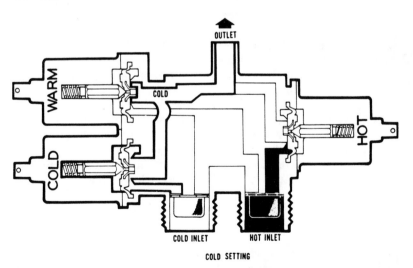

Fig. 3-22. Triple-solenoid shut-off valve.

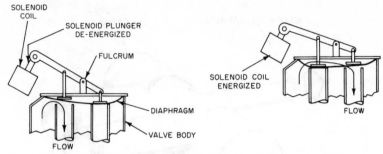

Fig. 3-23. Two-way suds return valve permits the re-use of wash water.

Triple solenoid shut-off valve (Fig. 3-22)—This valve permits four different wash temperatures—hot, medium, warm, and cold. It has a mixing chamber in which cold and hot water in varying amounts are combined to obtain the desired wash temperatures.

The actual temperature of the wash water depends on the temperature of the water in the hot-water tank and the temperature of the cold tap water. In a double-solenoid inlet valve, the temperature of a warm wash would be equivalent to half of the sum of tank water temperature and cold tap water temperature. For example, if tank temperature is 160°F, and the cold tap water is 50°F, the temperature of the water in a warm wash would be 105°F.

Two-way valves (Fig. 3-23)—Some washing machines employ a "suds return" system whereby the sudsy water from the first wash is stored in one of a pair of dual laundry tubs and is used again in a subsequent wash. If the customer selects the suds-return cycle, a solenoid is energized on the two-way valve to divert the drain water into the laundry tub instead of into the regular drain tub.

The solenoid is a "T" type, with a rubber diaphragm stretched over two ports. Energizing of the solenoid pulls down one end of a pivoted operating lever which presses a disc against the rubber diaphragm over the drain port, while the other end pulls a disc away from the rubber diaphragm over the suds return port. Normally, this valve directs the water flow into the drain port. Only sudsy water is stored in this system—rinse water is drained in the normal manner.

Water Pumps

The water pump (Fig. 3-24) operates continuously, receiving its power directly from the main drive belt. Most modern washers make use of a single-direction pump, meaning that the pump impeller rotates in only one direction for both discharge and recirculation. The recirculating impeller and the discharge impeller are located at opposite ends of the impeller shaft which drive both. In the suds-return machine, the pump may also be used to return the sudsy water into the machine from the storage laundry tub.

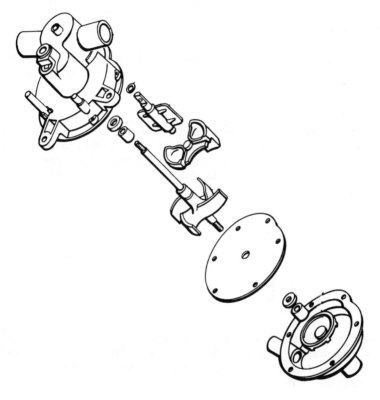

Fig. 3-24. Automatic washer water pump.

Filters

Many different kinds of filters are employed in the different makes of washing machines. However, their main purpose is to strain out lint and other foreign particles which are loosened from the clothing by the agitating action. These filters are sometimes placed in the discharge line, and are removable for periodic cleaning. Other machines locate the filter in the recirculation system at the top of the tub. Still others may have filters located on the agitator.

Hoses

Hoses are used extensively in washing machines to perform the main function of piping water from one component to another and to and from the machine itself. Inlet hoses are fitted with garden-hose fittings, sometimes incorporating screen filters which should be removed and cleaned periodically. The discharge hose is crimped and bent at the outlet end so that it may be conveniently hooked over the edge of the laundry tub.

Plastic hoses of small diameter are used to function as the compression chambers for the pressure-type fill switches discussed later.

Dispensers

Soap, bleach, and water softener dispensers are of many different kinds. Some are merely convenient receptacles which fit over the top of the agitator and permit the wash water to carry away the contents. Others are provided with sole-

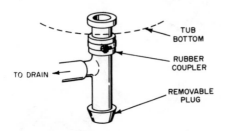

TUB BOTTOM

RUBBER COUPLER

TO DRAIN

REMOVABLE PLUG

Fig. 3-25. Trap assembly.

noids, timed so that they dump part or all of their contents into the wash water at various points in the wash cycle. These may also feature a rinse conditioner which is dispensed only during the rinse cycle.

Traps

Many washers are equipped with a trap assembly (Fig. 3-25). This serves to trap and hold any small objects which may otherwise circulate and damage the machine.

THE ELECTRICAL SYSTEM

With the exception of the combination washer/dryer, automatic and conventional washers employ a 115-volt, 60-cycle AC power source. Electricity is used not only to power the drive motor and the timer motor, but also the various electrical components used in controlling the flow of water in and out of the machine.

Typical wiring diagrams for an automatic washer and a combination washer/dryer are shown in Figs. 3-26 and 3-27. In the washer of Fig. 3-26, no provision is made for water temperature selection; the single solenoid serves as a shut-off valve only. The addition of another solenoid and an additional inlet valve on the hot-water line would make this a hot, cold, and warm water selection model.

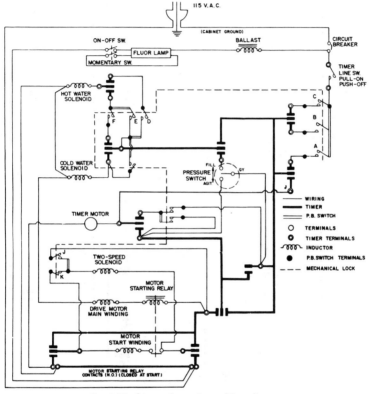

Fig. 3-26. Automatic washer wiring diagram

Note that the combination washer/dryer is an all electric model, using 220 volts to efficiently operate the heating element of the dryer circuit. The 115-volt line is used to power the drive motor and the other electrical components. (A gas-fired drying system may also be used in combinations.)

Since manufacturers may have upwards of a couple of dozen models of washers in their product lines, it would be

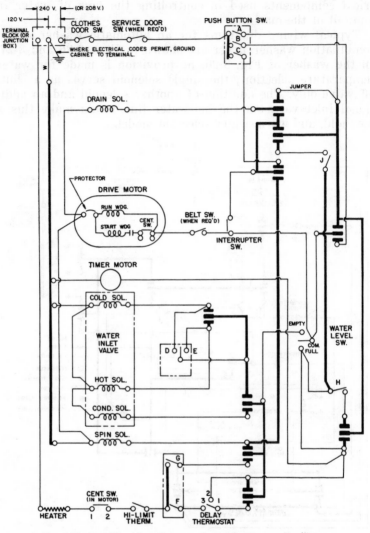

Fig. 3-27. Typical wiring diagram of combination washer/dryer.

impossible to show a wiring diagram for each model. If it is found necessary to consult the wiring diagram of a particular model, service literature may be obtained directly from the manufacturer's service department.

The following discussion of each of the common electrical components found in automatic washers will aid greatly in diagnosing and correcting electrical failures.

Timer

The timer (Fig. 3-28) is the heart of the control for all functions of an automatic washer. It consists of a synchronous motor (of the type usually found in clocks) which drives a pinion gear meshed with a drive gear in the timer assembly. This assembly may consist of a series of cam wheels or discs with inclined projections on their edges. As the cam wheels slowly revolve, cam surfaces rise to make contact with switch

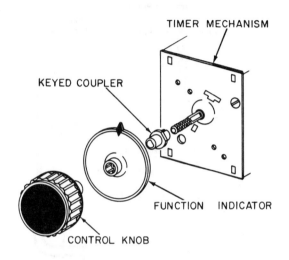

Fig. 3-28. Automatic washer timer mechanism.

levers, which in turn open or close electrical circuits to solenoids in the mechanical system. The length of arc of each cam surface, as well as its position on the cam wheel with respect to other cams on the same and other wheels is carefully planned so that the resulting action is accurately timed and synchronized.

A less common type of timer employs only one cam wheel, with switch arms located around its periphery. The cam wheel is perforated to accept pins actuated by pushbuttons. The pushbuttons offer the customer a selection of cycle variables, such as spin and agitation speeds, wash and rinse water temperatures, etc. As each pushbutton is depressed, it releases a pin against the side of the cam wheel. After the customer has selected the desired wash cycle, the dial is turned to the start position. This aligns the pins with the holes in the cam wheel, stopping the dial at the selected wash cycle. Now the user pushes the dial in to start the washer. This action pushes the pins out of the holes in the cam wheel, freeing it so that it can revolve under power from the timer motor.

Some washers and dryers are advertised as "Solid State" appliances. This is a reference to controls which take the form of thermistors for sensing heat in specific portions of the cycle. In a washer, the thermistor would be used to sense and regulate the heat of the incoming water. In certain dryers, a series

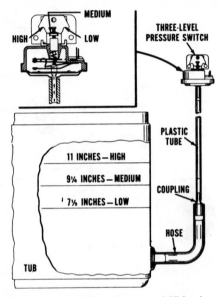

Fig. 3-29. Pressure switch used to control fill level.

of thermistors is used to register the temperature of air at the duct outlet, replacing bi-metal disc thermostats. Thermistors, due to their infinite settings potential, are more efficient in regulating temperatures than the off-on thermostatically controlled switch.

Fill Switches

Fill switches are of two types—pressure-actuated and float-actuated. In a pressure-actuated switch (Fig. 3-29), a plastic tube of small diameter is connected to a stand-pipe, the opening of which is near the bottom of the washer tub. As the water level rises, a bubble of air is trapped in the plastic tube and compressed. A diaphragm in the switch body becomes distended as the air pressure in the tube builds up, and at a preselected pressure it causes a pair of electrical contacts to separate, opening the circuit to the inlet valve solenoid, and cutting off the water supply.

A float switch (Fig. 3-30) is just what its name implies. A stand-pipe alongside the washer tub fills with water to the same level as the water in the tub. A float rides up and down in this stand-pipe; as it reaches its upper limit, it trips an operating arm connected to a switch and opens the electrical circuit to the inlet valve solenoid. As the water in the stand-pipe recedes, the weight of the float causes the switch to close so that water may be admitted when the timer completes the circuit.

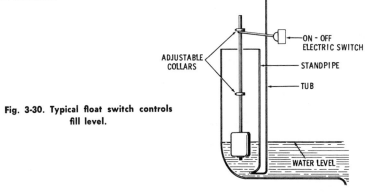

Fig. 3-30. Typical float switch controls fill level.

Generally speaking, washers equipped with float switches provide only one level of water, while those with pressure switches may provide three different levels, or even an infinite number of levels between high and low by means of settings on a dial. These settings change the distance that must be traveled by the diaphragm before the electrical contacts are opened. Pressure switches are calibrated at the factory and the adjustment screw normally sealed against field adjustment. A very small movement of the screw would materially change the water level in the tub, requiring very painstaking accuracy on the part of the field technician. Defective pressure switches should be replaced.

Fill switches, in addition to interrupting the current to the inlet-valve solenoids, are also in control of the other functions of the washer, since these other functions are dependent for their effectiveness on the proper water level (or absence of water) in the tub. When the fill switch is satisfied with respect to water level, it completes the circuits to the timer motor (the timer does not advance while the tub is filling initially) and the solenoid in control of the agitator. In addition, the fill switch also completes a circuit to the solenoid in control of the basket drive during the spin cycle. This latter circuit is completed when the pressure switch senses zero pressure, indicating that the tub is empty.

A typical cycle and the part played by the pressure fill switch is as follows:

During initial fill, only the circuits to the inlet-valve solenoids are completed, allowing water to enter the machine under its own faucet pressure. The drive motor and the timer motor do not operate during this period.

When the fill switch is satisfied, circuits to the inlet valve solenoids are interrupted and, at the same time, circuits to the drive motor and the timer motor are completed. The circuit to the agitator cam bar solenoid is completed through the action of cams on the timer motor which have been preset by the customer, and agitation begins without any further delay.

During the deep-rinse fill cycle, a by-pass circuit passes control of agitation to the fill switch. This means that even if the cams in the timer advance to the point where agitation would normally begin, the fill switch would not permit the circuit to be closed. On the other hand, should fill be accomplished *before* the cams advance to the proper point, no agitation will take place until the timer circuits were completed. This delay until a stated time period elapses is necessary to compensate for the difference in faucet water pressures, which result in longer or shorter fill time.

Lid Switch

A switch connected between the spin solenoid and the timer is attached to the clothes-loading door or lid of most washers so that spinning stops when the door is opened. This is a safety measure added to prevent accidents. Users have been known to add a garmet to the spinning clothes, with resultant serious injury as the powerful force generated by the heavy basket dragged both the garmet and flesh and bone into the machine. Mercury switches (Fig. 3-31) are popular for this use, since they are relatively simple and foolproof. A bubble of mercury normally rests in contact between two switch terminals when the lid is closed. As soon as the lid is opened even slightly, the bubble of mercury rolls away from the contacts and the circuit is instantly opened. This not only interrupts power to the basket-drive assembly, but it also applies the stop brake.

Solenoids

Solenoids (Fig. 3-32) are a means of converting electrical energy into mechanical energy to trip switches, open and close valves, and actuate mechanical linkages. Solenoids consist of a coil of wire in which a magnetic field is developed when current passes through it. This relatively powerful magnetic force is able to move a metal core or plunger resting inside the coil. Various arrangements of plunger, core, and coil exist, but the resulting action is always the same. The movement of the plunger is resisted either by a spring or by gravity, so that when the energizing current is switched off, the plunger returns to its normal position.

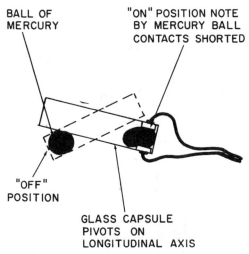

BALL OF MERCURY

"ON" POSITION NOTE BY MERCURY BALL CONTACTS SHORTED

"OFF" POSITION

GLASS CAPSULE PIVOTS ON LONGITUDINAL AXIS

Fig. 3-31. Mercury switch disconnects power to solenoid controlling spin.

Solenoids can do a certain amount of work, such as seating or unseating needle valves in liquid and vapor lines, but they do not generate enough force to engage gears or operate a heavy mechanism. Rather, they are used as the trigger—they start a train of events by setting free more powerful forces.

Defective solenoids are usually replaced rather than repaired, especially water-valve solenoids which are sealed at the factory to prevent the entry of water into their electrical components.

The functions of the agitator cam and basket-drive extractor cam solenoids have already been discussed in the section on the Mechanical System.

Drive Motor

The most popular type of motor used on washing machines is a ⅓ to ½ hp, 115-volt, 60-cycle, capacitor-start motor. These are equipped with thermal overload protectors which will disconnect the motor from the circuit if an overload condition occurs. These protectors re-set themselves when the

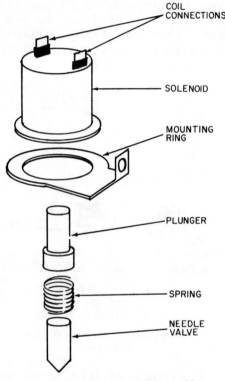

Fig. 3-32. A typical solenoid assembly.

motor has cooled sufficiently, and operation can resume. However, if the condition which originally caused the overload is not corrected, the overload protector will soon open the motor circuit again.

In washers equipped with a selection of two speeds, the drive motor is provided with two run windings. The wiring harness is connected to three terminals at the motor which permit selections such as Normal Action or Gentle Action to bring one or the other run winding into operation to achieve different speeds.

Service literature published by the manufacturers usually includes wattage ratings of the motor under both load and no-load conditions, which will be helpful in diagnosing some of the causes of failure. For a more detailed discussion of washing machine motors, see Chapter 11.

INSTALLATION

A good washer installation is important for two reasons— safety and satisfactory performance. Before beginning the installation, it is strongly recommended that the instruction booklet furnished by the manufacturer be read for any special instructions that may apply to that particular machine. The recommendations as to grounding and electrical connections must be followed faithfully to ensure a safe installation.

Most washers are equipped with shipping brackets fastened to the mechanical housing to prevent movement of the suspension system while in transit. Once the machine is installed, however, these shipping brackets must be removed before the washer is operated or damage to the machine may result.

Also, manufacturers recommend that if the machine is equipped with a two-speed motor, it be operated for the first time in the high-speed cycle. This is to prevent an overload to the motor as it attempts to start a transmission stiffened by long disuse. The greater power of the high-speed run windings is better able to overcome this stiffness.

Before the advent of the modern suspension system for the moving parts of the washer, an automatic had to be bolted down to the floor to prevent "creeping" as the tub revolved at the spin speed. In today's washers, however, this is rarely necessary. It is important, however, to ensure that the machine is level and supported by all four of the leveling legs, not just three. Check this by attempting to rock the machine diagonally in both directions.

Location

The best location for convenience and efficiency is alongside the laundry tubs. A single tub is all that is needed with standard washers, but those equipped with a suds-return feature require two—one to store the re-usable sudsy water from the first wash cycle, and another for the rinse water which is not stored but allowed to drain off. The tubs should be equipped with a stopper attached to a chain or other device operated from above the water level. Many housewives use the wash water to presoak, or to wash those clothes that are not color fast, outside the washer so as not to mix them with the regular wash. Reaching down into a tubful of water at or near 160°F to find the stopper is not such a good idea—hence the stopper chain.

The wash tub should be large enough to accommodate the entire high fill of approximately 18 gallons, with some capacity left over as a safety margin. Also, the drain should be fast enough to stay ahead of the washer drain—8 to 10 gallons per minute is a good drain rate.

Plumbing

For greatest efficiency, good water pressure is essential. Pressure giving a water supply of six to eight gallons per minute is usually adequate. A hot water source which maintains water at 160°F is best for satisfactory wash results. A hot water heater with a storage capacity of 30 gallons and a good recovery rate will be adequate. Water heaters with a relatively slow recovery rate, such as some electric models, should have a higher capacity for satisfactory operation.

Fig. 3-33. "Y" hose permits manual hot and cold water mix.

Most modern homes are equipped with hot and cold running water in the area designated as the laundry room. However, in homes that lack this convenience, it is necessary to install water lines to the washer. For washers with a single inlet hose (denoting the lack of a mixing valve) it will be necessary to use a "Y" hose (Fig. 3-33) which may be supplied by the washer manufacturer, or the installer might prefer to connect a mixing faucet to the hot and cold water lines. An extra set of faucets specially installed for the washer alone (Fig. 3-34) eliminates the attaching and disconnecting of hose lines—a condition leading to excessive wear. This also leaves the regular house faucets free for other uses.

The drain hose from the washer is constructed so that it will describe a natural curve in hooking over the edge of the laundry tub. Don't "fight" the curve by trying to force it into a different position. The recoil action of the water pour-

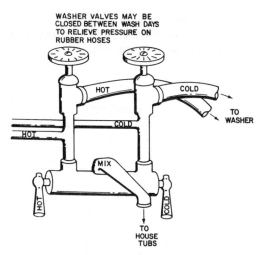

Fig. 3-34. Faucet installation makes easier automatic
washer operation.

ing out of the spout may push the hose off the edge of the tub
in subsequent washings, spilling gallons of hot, soapy water
on the laundry room floor.

Permanent plumbing connections are best achieved with
copper tubing of ⅜-inch O.D. Water-tight connections are
easily achieved by soldering all joints. If flexible copper tubing
must be used to get around awkward corners, be careful not
to kink it, as this will materially restrict the flow of water.
Measures should also be taken to prevent a flexible copper
tube from being kinked accidentally in subsequent use.

Flooring

The floor should be level or nearly so, and the machine
as level as it is possible to make it. A long carpenter's level
placed across both diagonals can be used as a check. If the
machine is installed above another room, be sure the floor
is sound enough to stand any vibrations that may occur from
an unbalanced load. If possible, shore up the floor from beneath to minimize shaking.

No matter how careful a customer may be, accidental water
spillage will occur at one time or another. For this reason,
floors should be in good condition at the start to minimize
any damage that may occur from these accidents. If asphalt
or plastic tile is used, it should be sound, with no holes where
water can gain entrance beneath the floor covering. Wooden
floors should be given two or three heavy coats of varnish and

95

wax before the installation is made. Any depressions or pockets where water can collect should be corrected beforehand, since it is virtually impossible to mop the floor underneath the machine.

Electrical Connections

Modern homes will have a convenient, grounded electrical outlet near the wash tubs. Some of these outlets are equipped with a three-prong receptacle to accept the three-pronged plug of the washer, the third prong being connected to the ground. Be sure the receptacle is actually grounded by testing as follows: Insert one probe of a tester in one hole of the outlet and touch the other to the cover-plate screw. If a test lamp, it should light—if a voltmeter it should read the full power-line voltage.

If the outlet is not grounded it will be necessary to run the ground wire provided by the manufacturer to the nearest cold water pipe. When this type of ground is used, the three-pronged plug may be used with a two-prong outlet by employing a special adapter. Local electrical codes will determine the advisability of using these adapters.

Electric combination washer/dryers will require a 220-volt power source in addition to the 115-volt source. These models are provided with a three-wire terminal block for convenience in making connections.

Gas combination washer/dryers will require plumbing connections to the gas supply pipe. It is a good idea when making this connection to provide an individual shut-off valve to the machine so that it may be isolated from the rest of the gas system whenever servicing is necessary. Joints must be carefully sealed to prevent the escape of even the smallest amount of gas. While a small gas leak may not constitute a serious threat to safety, it will be the source of a persistent odor. Test for leaks with an electronic leak detector, or with soap bubbles if the detector is not available. *Never test for inflammable gas leaks with an open flame!*

All combination units will require some means of venting to the outdoors (except those provided with a condenser lint trap). For venting suggestions, see Chapter 4.

WASHABILITY

The secret of a good wash is plenty of hot, "soft" water. Most manufacturers recommend water between 140°F and 160°F, although the higher figure is probably best for white clothes. Many housewives, especially those with younger children, are reluctant to have the temperature of the water hot enough to scald, citing safety and economy as reasons. In these cases, the customer should be informed that she will have to be satisfied with less than optimum results with her washer.

"Soft" or "hard" water is not a factor which can be controlled by the customer, but is rather a condition of the local water supply. Hard water (i.e., water with an abnormally high mineral content) will react with soaps and detergents to form a gray scum which lodges in the clothes. In areas with a hard-water problem, manufacturers recommend either the installation of a mechanical water softener or the addition of a water-softening chemical agent to the wash water.

Water hardness is measured in grains (or in parts per million). The average water hardness throughout the United States is approximately 10 grains. Any water measuring more than five grains of hardness should be softened. Soft water minimizes the amount of soap or detergent needed for good washability and, in addition, makes clothes last longer.

Automatic washers operate best with low-sudsing detergents. High-sudsing soaps can cause the tub to overflow under the action of the agitator. In addition, these soaps require a great deal more rinsing to wash them completely out of the clothes, necessitating a much greater amount of rinse water. It is for these reasons, rather than reasons of washability, that low-sudsing detergents are recommended for use in automatic washers.

Bleach should be used in the amounts recommended by the manufacturer. The customer should be cautioned to dilute the bleach with water before adding it to the wash water, if an automatic bleach dispenser is not provided. Bleach should never be added to the clothes until the tub is full, to avoid too strong a concentration.

Colorfast and noncolorfast clothes should never be included in the same wash. Test for colorfastness by squeezing a corner of the garment in hot suds. If color appears in the water, the garment is noncolorfast. After washing a noncolorfast garment which "runs" excessively, the washer should immediately be put through a complete cycle with hot water and detergent but without clothes.

Manufacturers usually provide complete instructions on washing techniques with the appliance. Customers should be cautioned to read the instructions thoroughly before attempting their first wash.

Performance Checks

Checking the performance of a washer to pinpoint the cause of failures requires checking a particular component at the time in the wash or rinse cycle at which it is *supposed* to operate. For example, if the inlet-valve solenoid is suspected of failure, the washer timer dial should be turned to the initial fill position, so that the electrical circuit to the solenoid is completed. Only then is it possible to test for continuity in the circuit. Similarly, if the agitator cam solenoid is suspected, the timer dial should be advanced to the wash cycle to complete the circuit to the agitator solenoid.

Mechanical failures in the washer's drive system will be evidenced by unusual noises and by the condition of the clothes on completion of the various cycles (still wet at the end of the spin cycle, etc.).

Common Failures and Replacements

Among the more common failures requiring the replacing of parts in automatic washers are:

Worn or broken drive belt—A loose belt is betrayed by a flapping noise throughout the cycling of the washer, and particularly when the machine is agitating or spinning. A broken belt, of course, results in no agitation, spin, or pumping, although initial fill will take place as usual. Replacement of the belt usually involves very little more than just slipping the new one over the motor pulley and the various drive pulleys, and adjusting tension. Tension adjustment is usually accomplished at the motor, by means of a slotted hole through which passes a motor mount bolt. Simply loosen the mounting bolt and pivot the entire motor until the proper tension is achieved. Drive belts should be tight enough to form a straight line between the pulleys, but not so tight that they cannot be flexed for an inch or two at the midway point between the various pulleys.

Defective timer assembly or motor—Timer assemblies are susceptible to wear because of their relatively fragile construction. Faulty timers may be detected by erratic functioning of the washer. Most timer trouble occurs at the switches, where burnouts, corrosion, and film deposits may cause open circuits or shorts. Normally, it is far easier and cheaper to replace a timer assembly than to attempt to repair it. The installation of a pushbutton timer requires synchronizing and indexing. Replacement timers are accompanied by detailed instructions for installation.

Pressure and float fill switches—Defective fill switches will be evidenced by incorrect water levels or by overflowing of the tub. Float switches, unless the stand-pipe is protected with a screen, are likely to become stuck by the introduction of small objects. One such case involved some gift pecans stored in the attic of the home, an exposed float-switch stand-pipe, and an enterprising squirrel with a hoarder's instinct, who found a way into the washer and stored the nuts in this very convenient contraption!

In most cases, the fault will lie with the fill switch itself, rather than with the float mechanism or the pressure chamber. Check for continuity by placing a test lamp in series with the switch terminals. Replace the switch if the continuity check is negative.

Control solenoids—In most cases, these will also fail due to a fault in the electrical components, rather than their mechanical elements. Check for continuity by placing a test lamp in series with the solenoid terminals. Faulty solenoids are detected by noting the absence of a particular function when it should occur, such as agitation, spin, or fill.

Drive motor—The first check of a drive motor is to see if it is receiving the proper voltage. This is done by disconnecting the leads to the motor and connecting them to a voltmeter. If the proper voltage is recorded when the timer dial is turned to On, the motor should be replaced. However, replacing the motor will certainly not eradicate the basic cause for the failure. Remember, motor burnouts don't just happen—they are caused. Here are some possible causes:

1. Extremely low-voltage conditions.
2. Loose electrical connections.
3. Binding in the motor bearings or the washer mechanism, or foreign particles in the motor switch.
4. Overload, evidenced by a high wattage reading.

Wattage Check

Checking wattage consumption of the washer with a wattmeter is a quick, easy way to determine if a condition exists which is putting an undue strain on the motor. Each brand and model of washer will have different wattage consumption norms, depending on the size of the motor, the capacity of the washer, and other variables. To get an accurate diagnosis, the technician must obtain a set of standard readings for the particular washer under study from a chart provided in the manufacturer's service literature.

No-load motor wattage—Slip the belt off the motor pulley and take a wattage reading with the timer dial in the high-speed (normal action) position. A ⅓ HP, 115-volt AC two-speed motor should read about 210 watts with no load and running on the high-speed winding. In some cases, manufacturer's literature will give wattage standards after the no-load wattage consumption has been subtracted. This is the case with the following wattage consumption examples.

Agitation wattage readings—With the basket (tumbler washers) revolving at approximately 60 rpm or the agitator operating at approximately 60 rpm, with the basket empty, wattage readings should be 200 watts; with high water level, water only, 300 watts; and with a full nine-pound load of clothes and water, the wattage reading should be 360 watts.

Pump-out wattage readings—With the tub empty, 250 watts; with the tub full, 325 watts.

Spin—With an empty basket (15 seconds to reach full speed), 300 watts; with a normal load (20 seconds to reach full speed), 375 watts; with the basket locked, 600 watts.

Wattages in excess of the values given, the time necessary to reach full speed in excess of the times given in the service literature, will indicate that an excessive load exists.

The following are some of the reasons for additional loads:

1. Pump clogged with foreign material, or impeller shaft binding.
2. Lack of lubrication at bearing surfaces or in gear case.
3. Drive belt bottoming in pulleys. Belts are intended to seat in pulleys so their outer edges are slightly higher than the edge of the pulley. *Bottoming* means that too much belt surface is coming in contact with the pulley, resulting in a drag. When belt is found to be bottoming, replace. Too tight an adjustment of the drive belt can also cause the same condition.

Too slow spinning may, of course, be due to binding in the mechanical train. However, it must be borne in mind that slow spinning can also be caused by belt slippage, which is in turn caused by oil or grease on the belt. The basket-drive clutch plate may also become fouled with oil, requiring cleaning or replacement.

TROUBLESHOOTING GUIDE

The following is a list of some of the more common failures, along with possible causes and their solutions.

No Water to Machine

1. Water faucets closed (it does happen).
2. Faulty inlet valve solenoid. If the hot water selection is made on a dial, and either the switch or the solenoid on the hot-water inlet valve is defective, water will not enter the machine, since the cold-water line is closed. Check continuity in the switch and solenoid and replace if either shows an open.
3. Open timer circuit. Replace timer assembly.
4. Open wiring harness circuit. Check between electrical components for continuity. Repair or replace broken wires.
5. Clogged inlet valve screen. Remove and clean screen. Be careful not to bend or distort the screen surface.
6. Defective water-level float or pressure fill switch. Check for electrical continuity and mechanical operation. Repair or replace as necessary.
7. Miscellaneous causes such as loose leads on electrical components, kinked hoses, trouble in the house water supply, etc. Make visual check to spot and correct trouble.

Motor Will Not Run

1. Branch-line fuse blown or circuit breaker tripped. Replace or re-set. Fuse may blow as a result of a temporary overload when two or more appliances start up at the same time. Check to determine whether branch line is carrying too many amperes. Connect affected appliance on different branch lines if necessary. This can be done by reconnecting the branch circuit at the main fuse box, or by running a separate line.
2. Overload protector tripped due to a thermal overload. Wait for thermal discs to cool, and then try motor again. If overload trips again, search elsewhere for overload condition.
3. No power to washer. Plug voltmeter into machine and line cord into voltmeter to check for line voltage. Replace line cord if indicated.
4. Inoperative motor. Disconnect leads to motor and connect them to voltmeter. If voltage registers, motor replacement is indicated.
5. Loose or disconnected leads to timer terminal block, etc. Tighten or make connections. Check all wiring.
6. Defective fill switch. Check and replace, if necessary.

Machine Will Not Agitate

1. Defective timer assembly. Check all leads for continuity. If no continuity exists between the common terminal and one or more of the other terminals in the assembly, timer must be replaced. If timer has separate motor which checks good, this part need not be replaced.
2. Faulty transmission. Make wattage test. If all other electrical tests are positive and wattage consumption is excessive, a mechanical fault in the drive mechanism is indicated. Transmissions of most washers may be repaired in the shop, first cleaning all parts to permit a careful visual check. It is not necessary to replace all the parts in the gear case—individual parts may be ordered by number by consulting manufacturer's literature. Check transmission parts for scoring, burrs, excessive wear, broken teeth and shafts, broken or worn seals, and gaskets.
3. Defective agitator solenoid. Check for continuity, mechanical freedom of movement of plunger, burrs on cam surfaces, slots, etc. Replace electrically defective solenoids, repair or replace mechanical parts as needed.
4. Inoperative motor, loose pulleys, defective fill switch, loose or disconnected leads, broken wiring, inoperative motor centrifugal switch. Take necessary action as indicated.

No Drain

1. Clogged drain pump or drain connections, loose or broken pump-impeller shaft, faulty flapper valves in pump. Low wattage with pump operating and water tub filled will indicate a broken impeller shaft. High wattage will indicate an obstruction in the pump or connections. Repair or replace as indicated.
2. Kinked drain hose, air lock, or suds lock. Air lock may be caused by baffle missing on tub at drain port. Suds lock is caused by excessive suds. Add cold water to tub and scoop out suds.

No Spin

1. Loose or broken belt. Inspect and replace or adjust. Grease or oil on clutch plate or on drive belt will result in slow spin, or no spin.
2. Faulty lid switch. Check for continuity with lid lowered. If no continuity, replace switch.

3. Defective spin solenoid. Check for continuity, replace if necessary. Check mechanical train triggered by solenoid for burrs, bent cams, etc.
4. Faulty water-level switch, broken wires, loose lead connections.

Excessive Vibration

1. Some washers have an unbalanced load cut-off switch which will stop the washer if an excessively unbalanced load occurs. In other machines, the washer may "walk" with an unbalanced load. Correct the walking by adjusting and tightening the leveling legs. The walking condition may also be caused by sympathetic vibrations being set up in a weakened floor. Correct the floor condition.
2. Damaged or misadjusted suspension system. Check to make sure that all suspension rods, motor mounts, rubber blocks, etc., are equally tight. Also check any gear-case braces or brackets that may have come loose.

Torn Clothes

1. Broken agitator, burrs on clothes basket. Inspect and replace, if necessary.
2. Overloading and the excessive use of bleach can cause damage to clothes. Check operating instructions.

Water or Machine Will Not Shut Off

1. Defective inlet valve or fill switch will cause overflowing. If fill switch opens at proper level and water continues above prescribed water level, faulty inlet valve is indicated. Also check wiring harness, timer, motor centrifugal switch, solenoid on inlet valve, and hoses.

Water and Oil Leaks

1. Check inlet and drain hoses for tight connections; pump gasket, gear-case gaskets and seals, tub gaskets and hose bodies for breaks.

TIMER SEQUENCE CHARTS

A wiring diagram of a washer cannot, all by itself, show the many combinations of open and closed switches, and the energized and de-energized electrical components throughout the cycling of the machine, since the switch positions change minute-by-minute as the timer advances. In order to fully

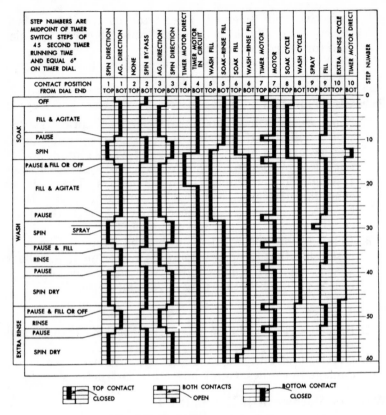

Fig. 3-35. Wash time sequence chart.

understand and trace the circuitry at any one moment in the cycling of the machine, it is necessary to study the wiring diagram in conjunction with a timer sequence chart, such as the one reproduced in Fig. 3-35. Many manufacturers provide some such chart in their service literature.

The timer contacts are listed across the top of the chart and identified so as to relate to the actual contacts on the timer cams. In the chart shown, the machine is controlled by pushbuttons. In this particular washer, each switch contact has a top and bottom position, which offers three possibilities—top contact closed, bottom contact closed, both contacts open. Leads are connected to the top and bottom contacts from the various electrical components of the machine.

On the left-hand side of the chart are listed the phases of the cycle—fill, soak, agitate, spin, and the various pauses between. At the right is a scale which indicates the timer-switch steps or increments. A value is given to each step by the note at the upper left-hand corner of the chart—in this case, each step is 45 seconds of time, or 6° on the timer dial.

If it is desired to trace the circuitry at any one moment in the cycling of the machine, lay a straight edge across the chart at the desired timer-dial step, or cycling phase. Now it is easy to tell which switch contacts are supposed to be open and which ones are closed at that particular phase of the wash cycle.

Turning to the wiring diagram, with a soft lead pencil or colored crayon fill in the switch contacts that are indicated as closed. All other switch contacts, of course, will be considered open. This now shows which electrical components are intended to be energized at that point of the timer advance.

CHAPTER 4

CLOTHES DRYERS

Clothes dryers accomplish drying by furnishing heated air in large volume into the interior of a rotating drum where the clothes are tumbled to expose all their surfaces to the passing air. Thus, a clothes dryer needs (1) a source of heat, (2) a means for tumbling the clothes, (3) a source for fresh air in large volume, and (4) a means of expelling moisture-laden air from the interior of the cabinet. In addition, dryers require controls for safeguarding clothes against extremes of heat and overdrying.

Fig. 4-1 is a block diagram which illustrates the operating pattern, as well as the general location of the main components of a dryer. The relatively dry air from the surrounding room enters the dryer cabinet through various vents in the front and back. A blower system forces this air through a flue arrangement where it is heated and then into the revolving drum through holes in the front face.

The bulk of the air circulates freely in the interior of the drum, passing through the tumbling clothes. The air in the interior of the drum soon approaches saturation, absorbing moisture from the clothes. The blower, which operates continuously while the drum is in motion, forces the moisture-laden air out through a vent leading outside the cabinet. Most dryers require further venting to the outdoors.

The principle of operation of a dryer strikes a balance between two contributing factors. The first is that heated air can absorb more moisture than cool air. Air at 32°F is capable of absorbing only about 2 grains of moisture per cubic foot. Air at 70°F can absorb about 8 grains of moisture, while air heated to 160°F absorbs 18.6 grains of moisture per cubic foot.

The second factor concerns the movement of air. Even if heated to 160°F, motionless air immediately adjacent to wet

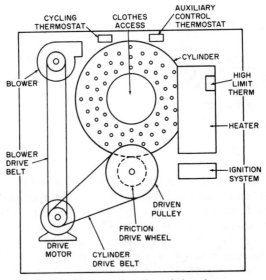

Fig. 4-1. Diagram of modern clothes dryer.

clothes will very quickly become saturated and unable to absorb any more moisture. If this air is replaced by currents of fresh, dry air, however, the moisture-absorbing process is hastened considerably.

By employing air that is both heated and moving (average temperature 160°F and moving at about 125-175 cfm) it is possible to hasten the natural drying process to a point where an efficient unit can remove approximately 10 lbs. of water (over 1 gal.) from a load of clothes in 1 hour. If the clothes are wrung out thoroughly before being placed in the dryer, a modern unit can dry a load of 19 or 20 lbs. (including the weight of the water) in about 1 hour.

DRYING PROCESS

Fig. 4-2 illustrates the temperature ranges encountered during a typical 1-hour drying process. (Temperatures listed in the chart are of the air inside the drum.) In this particular example, the drum air was heated to 150°F. Notice that the temperature drops as soon as the clothes are inserted and the cycle started. However, the temperature climbs quite rapidly to approximately 130°F, where it "plateaus," or maintains a fairly constant level throughout the next 40 or 45 minutes of drying time. Remember this *plateau* phenomenon—it will be useful when automatic drying is discussed later in this chapter.

As long as the clothes in the dryer remain fairly damp, the temperature of the interior will stay somewhere between 130°F and 145°F. This is due to a natural law which was mentioned in Chapter 2—evaporation of moisture is accompanied by cooling. As long as there is moisture in the clothes, evaporation is taking place. As long as evaporation is taking place, temperatures remain at a fairly low level.

After about 45 minutes of drying time, the clothes begin to lose their dampness and the temperature of the exhaust air begins to rise sharply, climbing rapidly to 160°F. At this

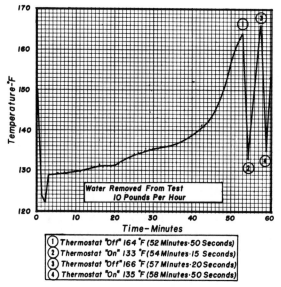

① Thermostat "Off" 164 °F (52 Minutes·50 Seconds)
② Thermostat "On" 133 °F (54 Minutes·15 Seconds)
③ Thermostat "Off" 166 °F (57 Minutes·20 Seconds)
④ Thermostat "On" 135 °F (58 Minutes·50 Seconds)

Fig. 4-2. Progression of temperature readings inside the drum of a dryer during one-hour drying cycle.

point a temperature-sensing device, which may be a bimetal disc, snaps open, and the current which initiates the heat-generating component, whether gas or electric, is cut off and the temperature subsides.

If the housewife attempted to remove the clothes from the dryer at this time, she would find that most items would be unacceptably damp. The blower motor continues to run, however, until a low point in temperature is reached where the temperature-sensing device again closes the circuit to the heater, causing the temperature to start rising. This continues, in clock-timed dryers, until the timer runs out at the end of its set period, or until the operator shuts off the machine.

The majority of dryers depend on a timer mechanism for their cycling. The timer is set by the user so that at the end of the period selected the clothes will be dried to the desired degree. The length of time set will depend on the amount and kind of clothes to be dried. Customers are instructed (in the operating manual) to include only items of similar weights and textures in any one load whenever possible, so that the entire load will dry to the same degree at the end of the period. If light and heavy fabrics are included in the same load, the light fabrics will dry faster. The result is that, if the dryer is allowed to cycle until the heavy fabrics are dry enough, the light fabrics will be "bone dry," a condition that causes excessive wrinkling.

Under normal conditions, all fabrics contain moisture amounting to about 5% of their total weight. This is a desirable condition, making the fabrics soft and pliant. Those containing no moisture tend to be stiff and brittle and are far more difficult to iron.

AUTOMATIC DRYING

Many of the modern gas and electric dryers are billed as "automatic" models, shutting themselves off when the clothes reach a point where moisture content is reduced to an acceptable minimum. Rather than sensing the moisture content, however, automatic drying is accomplished by an auxiliary control thermostat working in series with the regular cycling thermostat. These thermostats sense heat increase and decrease only—they do not react to moisture content directly. Both thermostats are placed in the path of the air exhausted from the dryer.

To understand the functioning of a typical automatic system, refer to Fig. 4-3, which is a schematic diagram of a gas dryer. Note the locations of the cycling thermostat, the high-limit thermostat, and the auxiliary cut-off thermostat.

The cycling thermostat is preset to open or close two different electrical circuits. At approximately 130° F, the thermostat will close in position 1-2. At 120° F the thermostat will close in position 1-3 activating the gas solenoid. Remember that the temperature of the air in the dryer will remain at a fairly constant level as long as there is a high level of moisture in the clothes. (Note: The temperatures will be somewhat lower in the example chosen for this description of automatic drying

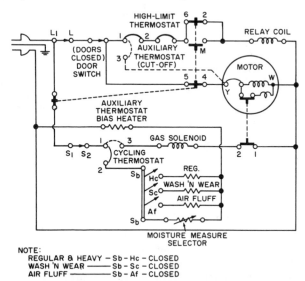

Fig. 4-3. Schematic diagram of an automatic drying system.

than those shown in Fig. 4-2. The reason for this is that the temperatures in the table were taken at the drum's interior, while those referred to here are read in the exhaust flow path.) When the moisture content of the clothes in the dryer starts to fall, the exhaust temperature will begin to move above the plateau level. When it reaches 130° F, the cycling thermostat will close in the 1-2 position, opening the circuit to the gas solenoid (or heater coil). A flow of current reaches the bias heater of the auxiliary control thermostat (Fig. 4-4). The bias heater warms the bimetal switch of this thermostat, which is set to open at 150° F and close at 130° F.

Before the current reaches the auxiliary control thermostat, however, it must pass through a resistance set up by a potentiometer placed in series with the thermostat bias heater.

In parallel with the potentiometer will be one of three fixed resistors of either 2000, 1150, or 500 ohms. These are placed in the circuit by pushbutton switches which permit the customer to select longer or shorter drying periods.

After passing through the potentiometer, the current reaches the bias heater of the auxiliary control thermostat, causing its heat to increase toward 150° F. This heater will draw more or less current, depending on the selection made by the customer to generate a greater or lesser amount of heat. This, in turn, causes the auxiliary control thermostat to cut off in a longer or shorter time, respectively.

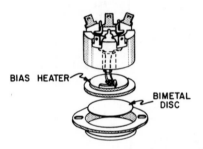

BIAS HEATER

BIMETAL
DISC

Fig. 4-4. The auxiliary control thermostat with bias heater element.

In a regular cycle, the air-flow temperature will drop to 120° F sooner than the ambient heat of the auxiliary control thermostat can reach 150° F because the clothes still contain a large amount of moisture. This causes the switch contacts of the cycling thermostat to close again in position 1-3, turning the gas heater on again, and interrupting the current to the bias heater of the auxiliary control thermostat. The dryer continues to cycle, and again the heat in the exhaust air flow begins to climb, this time more rapidly than before because there is now less moisture in the clothes.

The temperature again reaches 130° F, and the cycling thermostat again snaps into the 1-2 position, causing a flow of current through the potentiometer and to the bias heater of the auxiliary control thermostat. With the main heater off, the air in the exhaust air flow will begin to cool, but the ambient heat of the auxiliary control thermostat will again start approaching the 150° F cutoff temperature.

Before it reaches cutoff, however, the dryer will once again go into its heating cycle if the exhaust air temperature reaches 120° F before the auxiliary control thermostat senses 150° F. Each succeeding heat-on cycle, however, will be shorter and shorter until the 150° F mark is finally reached by the auxiliary control thermostat.

When this point is reached, the bimetal disc (similar to those used in overloads) will snap the auxiliary control thermostat into the 1-3 position and the relay holding contacts will open, dropping the relay out of the circuit. This opens both the heater and motor circuits. However, the 1-3 position of the auxiliary control thermostat provides a second path for current to reach the motor for a "cool-down" period (the motor turns the clothes drum and the blower, but the heater is off). When the auxiliary control thermostat cools down to 130°F, the bimetal disc will return the contacts to the 1-2 position (to the path of the open relay) and the machine will shut itself off.

The high-limit thermostat shown in the diagram is provided in both gas and electric models, whether automatic or timed. In gas models it is set to open the relay circuit when the temperature in the burner duct reaches approximately 275°F, and closed when the temperature drops back to 195°F.

In electric models the high-limit switch is opened when the temperature in the heater housing reaches approximately 210°F, and closed when the temperature drops to 160°F.

A restriction in the air flow caused by a clogged lint trap or a blocked duct may activate the high-limit switch in either gas or electric models. Failure of either the auxiliary control thermostat or the cycling thermostat can also cause the high-limit contacts to open.

GAS DRYERS

The controls and heater assembly (Fig. 4-5) of a gas dryer are far more complex than the comparable components in

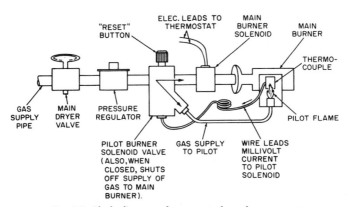

Fig. 4-5. Block diagram of gas controls and components.

113

electric models because of the requirement of a pilot flame and the on and off cycling of the gas flow to the main burner.

In order to start the gas dryer, it is first necessary to light the pilot burner. This is accomplished either by applying a flame to the pilot burner or, as in some models, by means of an electric "spark plug" or platinum coil. In either case, the flame of the pilot burner heats a thermocouple which generates a small electrical current. This current is strong enough to hold the plunger of a solenoid valve in the open position, permitting gas to flow to the pilot (and to the main-burner solenoid valve as well). In flame-lit pilots, the flame remains burning as long as the main gas-supply valve is turned on. Pulling the power cord from the wall outlet will not cause the pilot flame to go out, since the electrical current that holds the solenoid pilot valve open is self-generated in the thermocouple. In models with coil-lit pilots, however, the timer interrupts the current to both the main motor and to a 24-volt circuit which supplies current to both the main-burner solenoid and the pilot solenoid. In this case, the pilot flame goes out when the drying cycle is completed.

By turning the timer mechanism (which may be either spring-loaded or motor-driven) contacts are closed, causing current to be applied to the main motor. It starts, actuating both the clothes drum and the blower fan. When the motor has reached approximately 1400 rpm, a centrifugal switch on the motor housing closes the circuit to the main-burner solenoid. On the same circuit with the centrifugal switch is the high-limit thermostat, the cycling thermostat, and the auxiliary control thermostat. Since temperatures within the dryer at the moment of start are below normal operating temperature, the main-burner solenoid is permitted to open by the various controlling thermostats (normally closed), and the main burner ignites.

Air flow set up by the blower system draws air into a flue below the main burner duct, where it is heated and enters the revolving drum through holes in its faces. The warmed air circulates through the clothes which are tumbling in the drum, and then is drawn through the blower and out the exhaust duct. As the exhaust air passes through the exhaust duct, its temperature is sensed by the cycling thermostat. When the temperature of the exhaust air begins to climb as the clothes approach the final stages of drying, the cycling thermostat opens the circuit to the main-burner solenoid and closes a circuit to the auxiliary control thermostat. Now follows a cool-down period followed by a heat-on period, until

114

either the timer mechanism or the achievement of shut-off temperatures in the automatic system shuts off the dryer.

Components

Following is a list of the main components of a typical gas dryer, with a description of their functioning.

Power-cord plugs—These are usually of the three-prong type, the third prong being a cabinet ground. Most appliances are provided with an alternate ground wire and harness for attaching to the nearest suitable ground. Local electrical codes will spell out whether or not adapters for wall outlets may be used along with the alternate ground harness.

Fig. 4-6. Main-burner gas solenoid.

Motors—Dryer motors are usually ¼ to ⅓ hp, 115-volts, 60-cycle, split-phase types of approximately 1,725 rpm. Gas dryers, unlike electric, require only regular 115-volt house current for operation. A shaft protruding from both ends of the motor provides a power take-off for the revolving drum on one end and the blower on the other.

Main-burner gas solenoids—These may be actuated by either 115 or 24-volt current, the latter being stepped down by a transformer. The gas solenoid (Fig. 4-6) is wired in series with the control thermostats and the centrifugal switch. The centrifugal switch is extra insurance against dangerous build-up of high heat, opening the main-burner valve only after the motor has attained run speed.

Timers—Timers may be driven by a spring-wound clock mechanism or by an electric motor (Fig. 4-7A). Fig. 4-7B shows the arrangement and method of operation of a typical cam used in these timer mechanisms.

Automatic controls—These controls for heavy and light loads, etc, are normally of the potentiometer type, permitting selection of various degrees of resistance ahead of the auxiliary control thermostat. By reducing or increasing amperage,

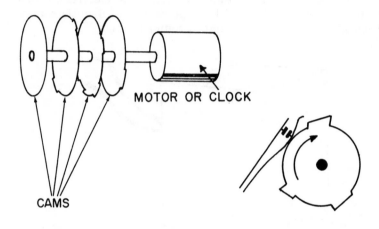

(A) Cam-driving mechanism.   *(B) Typical cam and contact.*

Fig. 4-7. Dryer cam-operated timer.

the wattage consumption of the bias heater of the auxiliary control thermostat is carefully controlled, causing the auxiliary control thermostat to open later or sooner as a means of controlling the length of the heat-on cycle.

Thermocouples—When the pilot burner is lighted, a hot and cold junction of the two metals iron and nickel (Fig. 4-8) creates a current, measured in millivolts of electricity, in a coil around the solenoid valve plunger. The current is sufficient to hold open the plunger, though not sufficiently strong to overcome the force of a spring initially. Thus, it is necessary to press a button to hold the plunger open against the force of the spring until the thermocouple joint warms up sufficiently (about 20-30 seconds) after which the small thermocouple-generated current is sufficient to hold up the solenoid.

Any momentary interruption of this small current will cause the solenoid plunger to close the valve, shutting off the supply of gas to both the pilot and the main burner. This valve will not reopen by itself—the start button must be pressed again and a flame applied to the pilot burner.

"Spark plugs" or glow coils—A 24-volt transformer supplies current to a 24/2.5-volt transformer which energizes a glow coil located at the pilot burner. The current causes the coil of platinum wire to give off an intense heat, sufficient to ignite the gas coming out of the pilot burner. Once ignited, the gas flame is directed against a bimetal strip, which instantly snaps to the open position, interrupting the flow of current to the glow coil. The extremely low voltage is necessary because a higher potential would quickly burn out the fine platinum wire.

Pressure regulators—These devices are for regulating the escape pressure of the gas entering the dryer and are normally preset at the factory for 3½" water column pressure. Adjustments may be made, when necessary, by means of an adjusting screw. Follow the instructions in the manufacturer's literature, using a manometer for precise measurement of the gas pressure.

Burner orifices—Different types of gas (natural, manufactured, LP., etc.) require different orifices. Dryers shipped to areas using a particular type of gas normally have the proper orifice already installed. The wrong orifice will greatly affect the Btu heat input of the burner.

Main-burner solenoid valve—These valves control the flow of gas to the main burner and are wired in series with and controlled by the auxiliary control and high-limit thermostats. If the contacts of either thermostat are in the open position, the flow of current to the normally closed solenoid will be interrupted. When the contacts of both thermostats are in their normally closed position, a flow of current creates a magnetic field around the solenoid plunger, causing it to react against the force of a spring to open the gas valve.

The pilot-burner solenoid valve is located ahead of (in terms of gas flow) the main-burner solenoid so that if the pilot flame should go out and the thermocouple current to the pilot solenoid valve is interrupted, both the main and pilot-burner gas supply will be shut off.

High-limit thermostats—The function of the high-limit thermostat is to interrupt the current to the heater should the temperature of the heater housing exceed a preset limit. In some models, the high-limit thermostat also shuts off power to the drive motor so that the dryer must be restarted. This is an extra insurance against overheating.

High-limit thermostats are usually preset at the factory, with no field adjustment possible. In gas models, the high-limit is set at approximately 275°F ±7°F.

Cycling thermostats—In automatic models, normally closed cycling thermostats are used in conjunction with auxiliary control thermostats having bias heaters. The automatic types are preset at lower cut-on and cut-off temperatures than the timer-model dryers. No adjustment of temperature range in the field is possible.

When in the closed position, cycling thermostats pass current directly to the main-burner solenoid. When in the open

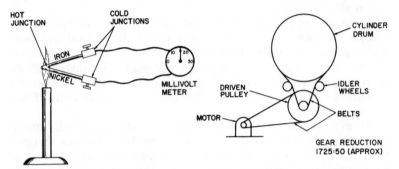

Fig. 4-8. A thermocouple.   Fig. 4-9. Clothes-dryer cylinder-drive system.

position, the current is diverted to the flow path in which the auxiliary control thermostat is located, opening the circuit to the main heater.

Auxiliary control thermostats—These are of two types—the standard bimetal, normally closed, disc type, and the bimetal, normally closed, disc type with built-in bias heater.

The function of the auxiliary control thermostat is to open the circuit to the heater when its high limit (usually 20° or 30° higher than the cycling thermostat) is reached. When its low limit is reached, it closes the circuit to the heater, "passing the ball" again to the cycling thermostat for another heat-on cycle.

In some auxiliary control thermostats, the high limit causes it to snap into a position that opens a relay circuit to the heater, but provides a second path to the drive motor for a short "cool-down" period. When the low limit is reached after the cool-down period, the contacts snap back into the already-open relay circuit and the machine is completely shut off.

Cylinder drive assemblies—To reduce the 1,725 rpm achieved by the drive motor to the 50 rpm (approximately) at which the clothes drum must revolve, a speed reduction system is required. One such system is shown in Fig. 4-9, in which the motor pulley drives a driven pulley, which in turn drives the drum. In a variation of this method (Fig. 4-10), the motor pulley is connected to the drum through a jackshaft. The outside circumference of the drum's drive wheel is rubber, causing the drum to revolve by means of friction.

In earlier models, a belt switch is employed as a safety measure to protect against the dangerous build-up of heat should any of the belts break. The normally open switch (Fig. 4-11) is closed by a spring-loaded plunger which is kept in the closed position by the tension of the belt. If the tension should be relieved, as in the case of a broken or excessively loose belt, the spring forces the plunger to open the switch. This switch is connected in series with the main burner solenoid, thus shutting off the supply of gas.

The same protection is now afforded by the high-limit thermostat used in later models, which senses heat build-up and shuts off the main burner as well as the drive motor.

Clothes Doors—Most dryers employ a door switch which shuts off both heat and drive motor when the door is opened. In some models, the service door is also protected in the same manner (Fig. 4-12).

Accessories

Germicidal lamps are used in some dryers because of their germ-killing power. These are usually connected in series with the initiator mechanism.

Lint filters are provided with all dryers. These are designed to trap and hold lint which is shaken loose from clothes as

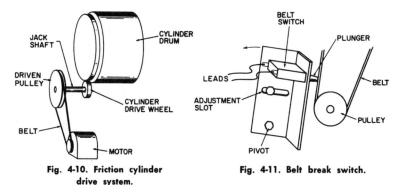

Fig. 4-10. Friction cylinder
drive system.

Fig. 4-11. Belt break switch.

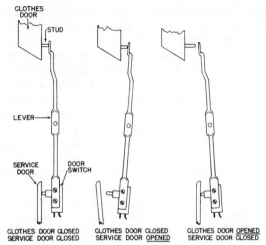

CLOTHES DOOR CLOSED
SERVICE DOOR CLOSED

CLOTHES DOOR CLOSED
SERVICE DOOR OPENED

CLOTHES DOOR OPENED
SERVICE DOOR CLOSED

Fig. 4-12. Door interlock switch arrangement.

they are tumbled about in the drum; however, lint escapes from even the most ingenious traps, simply because the exhaust air cannot be restricted too much without impairing the efficiency of the unit.

Vent kits (Fig. 4-13) are available, either for a particular model, or universal types to fit all models. In venting to the outdoors, it is important that the dryer be located near an outside wall through which the vent pipe may be easily led. It is recommended that not more than four right-angle turns be made in the exhaust pipe, which may vary from 3 to 4 inches in diameter, depending on the dryer model. If four right angles are made in the exhaust pipe, not more than

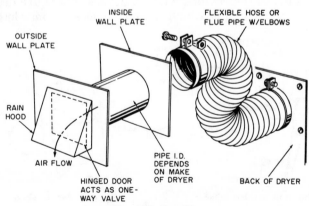

Fig. 4-13. Vent kit.

120

20 ft. of straight pipe should be used to reach the outdoors. For two right angles, a maximum of 25 ft. of straight pipe may be used.

Some models of automatic dryers wash the lint produced by the dryer down the water drain. They accomplish this by passing the exhaust air through a condenser through which cold faucet water flows. As the air encounters the cold surfaces of the condenser, the moisture it contains condenses to liquid, carrying with it the tiny particles of lint that have escaped the lint filter. The condensate and the lint particles are washed down the drain by the same water that is used to cool the condenser.

ELECTRIC DRYERS

Electric dryers differ from gas models mainly in the source of heat, using an electrical heating element in place of the open gas flame. However, there are a few other differences.

The schematic diagram in Fig. 4-14 traces the circuitry of a typical electric dryer employing a timed drying cycle. Note that the dryer requires a three-wire 230-volt power source for most efficient operation. It is possible to run the 230-volt heating element on standard 115-volt current by shifting one wire to the neutral line, as noted in Fig. 4-14, running only two wires to the power source. This, of course, cuts down the efficiency of the dryer by about half, which means that clothes will take twice as long to dry. It is not recommended practice.

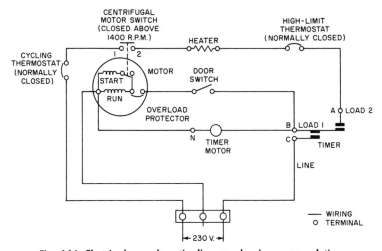

Fig. 4-14. Electric dryer schematic diagram, showing a manual timer.

121

A 230-volt dryer also requires a standard 115-volt circuit to drive the motor and the controls. This is obtained by using two of the three wires as shown in Fig. 4-15. Some electric dryers also make use of a 24-volt current, obtained by means of a transformer, to power the thermostat controls. A 24-volt current makes it possible to use less hefty components, thus cutting the costs of manufacture.

The thermostatic controls of a typical electrical dryer are very much the same as those found in a gas dryer, with the exception that the contacts are wired directly to the heater, rather than energizing solenoid valves to open or cut off gas

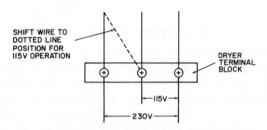

Fig. 4-15. Method of converting a 230-volt dryer to 115-volt operation.

flow. The cycling thermostat is played against the auxiliary control thermostat to alternate heat-on cycles with cool-down cycles until the clothes are dry enough to raise the temperature of the interior of the drum to open the circuit, or until the time selected on the timer motor has run out.

There is one other method of achieving automatic drying which is used on electric dryers. This is called a combination timed and automatic operation. In this method, the timer motor is energized only during the cool-down periods, being taken out of the circuit by the auxiliary control thermostat during heat-on periods. When a sufficient amount of time (about 20 minutes) has accumulated on the timer, the dryer goes into a final cool-down period of about 10 minutes and shuts itself off.

The cool-down cycle is reduced or lengthened to vary the drying time of heavy loads, different fabrics, etc.

The heating element (Fig. 4-16) may be located in various places around the drum, the most widely used location being around the entire circumference at one edge. The element consists of a coil of wire through which flows the 230-volt current. Most such heaters are rated at from 4,000 to 5,000 watts at 230-volts. The heater is mounted in such a position that the

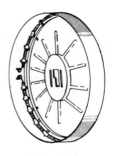

Fig. 4-16. Heating element of a 230-volt dryer.

air entering the clothes drum must first pass over its coils. In electric dryers, the high-limit thermostat is located at or near the heater housing.

Repairs to the heater elements are not usually considered economically feasible. If an element fails, it is better to replace the entire heater assembly.

Fig. 4-17 shows a typical hook-up of an electric dryer. Note the use of No. 10 wire in the hook-up (if the dryer is located more than 60 feet from the main fuse box, use No. 8 wire). Electric dryers should be connected to a separate branch circuit with no other appliances on the same line. Fusing should be a minimum of 30 amperes.

Performance Checks

Checking the performance of a dryer, apart from the obvious visual checks, is largely a matter of taking its pulse and

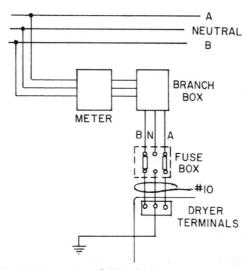

Fig. 4-17. Connection of 230-volt dryer to power source.

temperature. Wattage readings, like pulse readings, will tell whether the components themselves are functioning properly. Temperatures at the exhaust air duct taken at the appropriate time in the drying cycle will give additional information which can be used to double-check the wattage findings.

An experienced technician, as in all appliance repairing, relies heavily on the evidence of his senses in diagnosing trouble. He touches the air ducts to feel how hot they are; he looks for signs of wear on belts and other moving parts; he listens for telltale sounds that indicate some abnormal condition; he even smells for trouble such as gas leaks, heater and motor burnouts, etc.

All dryers employ essentially the same basic principle for their operation, as outlined at the beginning of this chapter. But different makes and models may differ very widely from each other in the details of horsepower, wattage, cut-out and cut-in temperatures, and air velocity, as well as types of timers, heaters, thermostats, regulators, valves, and other components. It would be quite beyond the scope of this book to attempt to define all the performance checks and ratings for each particular make and model.

However, the standards of performance of each dryer are usually published by the manufacturer in his service literature. This literature will list the actual rating figures for wattages, voltages, resistances, and temperatures. The following describes how these values are applied to the performance of the dryer being checked.

Temperature and operating check—If the dryer is a new installation, be sure to follow the manufacturer's instructions as to uncrating, removing shipping blocks, checking for loose wires, etc. Turn the unit on. If the dryer is run empty, add about 10°F-15°F to the values given in the manufacturer's ratings with full load.

Insert a thermometer (bimetal type, range 100° to 200°F) in the exhaust air flow well inside the exhaust duct (Fig. 4-18). Read temperatures during the heat-on cycle as well as during cool-down. When reading temperatures, use the highest reading during heat-on, the lowest reading during cool-down.

Readings of exhaust temperatures will be affected by the temperature of the room in which the dryer is located. Most performance standards take this into account, giving standard readings at different ambient temperatures.

Wattage checks—Wattage checks are taken of the heater in electric dryers, as well as bias heaters in gas and electric auxiliary control thermostats (Fig. 4-19). Wattage readings

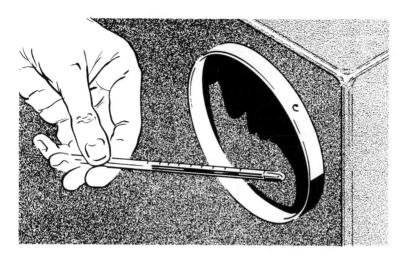

Fig. 4-18. Method of taking temperature readings at the dryer exhaust duct.

of the latter with a variance of 10% or more from the published standard indicate that replacement is required.

In addition, wattage readings may be taken of the drive motor under full or no load. Abnormally high wattage readings of the motor mean that (1) some abnormal binding condition

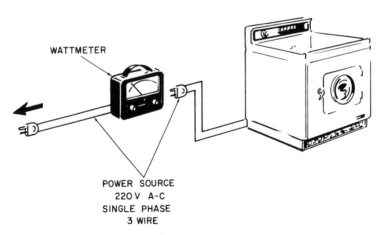

DRYER

WATTMETER

POWER SOURCE
220 V A-C
SINGLE PHASE
3 WIRE

Fig. 4-19. How to make a wattage check of electric dryer heater.

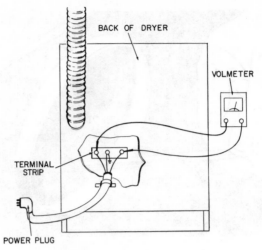

BACK OF DRYER

VOLMETER

TERMINAL STRIP

POWER PLUG

Fig. 4-20. Voltage check of electric dryer.

exists in the cylinder drive system or the blower system, and (2) a serious obstruction exists in the air flow ducts.

Wattage checks are made according to the directions given in Chapter 1.

Ohmmeter readings—Measuring the ohms of resistance in components such as thermostats and solenoid valves will uncover shorts or leaks.

Amperage readings—To discover shorts in the wire harness, a fast, simple check may be made by using a hook-on ammeter (see Chapter 1).

Voltage check—Particularly in electric dryers it is important that rated voltages be supplied to the dryer (Fig. 4-20). A 230-volt dryer will not operate as efficiently (resulting in slower drying) if the voltage supplied measures only 208 volts. Power supply voltages are read at the entrance to the dryer. If an exceptionally long lead is required from the power source to the dryer (60 ft. or more) the next larger size wire than that recommended by the manufacturer should be used.

Some manufacturers supply transformer kits to step up or step down voltage from 208-230 volts or 230-208 volts. These kits are generally accompanied by detailed installation instructions and a wiring diagram.

Common Failures and Replacements

Failures in dryers occur most often in the moving parts of the cylinder drive system. One of the most frequently encountered failures is a worn out drive belt. Excessive belt wear may be caused by binding at the pulley bearing, or too much or too little belt tension. To correct or prevent binding conditions at the pulley be sure to lubricate it properly. See Chapter 1 for tips on lubrication.

Belt tension may be checked visually. The belt should be tight enough to form a straight line where it travels from one pulley to the next. It should not be so tight that you cannot flex it slightly at the mid-point between pulleys with a slight squeeze. Be careful not to get oil in the pulley grooves or on the belt itself when lubricating. Oil deteriorates rubber.

Another common failure in dryers is a motor burnout. However, motor burnouts don't just happen—they are caused. When replacing the motor of any appliance, look for a reason for the failure. Among the more common causes for a motor burnout are a defective overload protector, loose or shorted wiring in the appliance, as well as within the motor itself, binding in the moving parts and fusing or house wiring defects. Be sure the branch-wire fuses are of the proper rated amperage as given on the dryer nameplate.

A less frequent cause of trouble may be found in the venting system. An excessive amount of lint build-up will interfere with the free flow of air through the dryer. A dislocation of an air duct may cause the escape of lint to the moving parts of the dryer.

Venting systems have also been known to "blow back." Strong or gusty winds from the outdoors may enter the dryer through the exhaust vent outlet and actually blow out the pilot flame. The exhaust vent should be provided with a hinged aluminum door that will only permit the outward flow of air. Be sure the door moves freely under light pressure so the exhaust air flow will not be restricted.

Timer motors tend to fail after long use. Contacts may burn out or internal circuitry may become shorted or leaky. Replacement of the entire component is usually the best course.

In gas dryers the most frequent cause for failure in the gas system is the pilot-burner solenoid valve.

TROUBLESHOOTING GUIDE

Before any repairs or disassembly are attempted on a dryer, the power cord should be pulled from the wall outlet—especially important in electric dryers, because of the high voltages developed and because dryers are frequently located on basement floors in direct contact with the ground. When checking components, such as heaters with the dryer partially disassembled, turn on the timer motor to the appropriate point in its cycle and then plug in the power cord without touching the cabinet or other components. Testing for shorts of individual components or wiring harness with an ohmmeter or test lamp may be accomplished in most cases without turning the dryer on.

Following are some of the more common signs of trouble in a dryer, both electric and gas, and the probable causes and remedies. It is by no means a complete list, but should serve as a guide to solve most of the problems encountered.

Dryer Does Not Start

1. Power failure. Look for blown fuse, breaks in house wiring, power cord or defective power-cord plug. If the fuse is blown, look for underlying causes, such as high voltage, another appliance on the same branch line, etc. Merely replacing a fuse does not correct the cause of failure.
2. Defective motor, door switch, or timer motor. Apply test lamp to component leads to check for shorts. Press door switch button manually with dryer turned on to check for mechanical defect. Replace or repair as necessary.
3. Loose connections at components or terminal block. Check segments of wire circuitry with test lamp.
4. Inoperative or defective high-limit thermostat. Thermostat is normally closed, will permit current flow at temperatures below danger level. Test thermostat leads with ohmmeter or test lamp. If contacts are open at less than rated cut-out temperature, thermostat is defective and should be replaced.

Motor Runs But Drum Does Not Turn

1. Loose or broken drive belt; pulley loose on drive shaft. Make necessary repairs or replacements.

No Heat, Drum Turns

1. In electric dryers, look for defective circuitry at or near the heating element and within the heating element coil itself. Test for shorts with test lamp.
2. In gas dryers, look for a defective pilot-burner solenoid valve or a defective main-burner solenoid. These components are generally sealed and must be replaced as an assembly. Also check gas supply lines and main valve.
3. Check for a defective open or shorted cycling thermostat or auxiliary control thermostat. Manufacturer's litera-

ture will give the proper ranges of these thermostats, as well as approved test procedures for testing bias heaters in auxiliary control thermostats. The range of a thermostat may become disturbed without causing the thermostat contacts to test open or short. If this is suspected, the thermostat should be replaced.

4. In earlier models, a worn or loose belt may cause the protective belt switch to function, shutting off the flow of current to the electric heater or to the main gas burner solenoid valve.

Dryer Will Not Shut Off

1. Inoperative or defective clock timer or timer motor. A bent stop pin on the timer dial may prevent the dial from rotating all the way to Stop. Burned out contacts in the timer may also cause this symptom. Check also for shorting of the timer internal circuitry as well as the drive motor.

Slow Drying

1. Improper loading. Overloading, or loading clothes into the dryer that are not thoroughly wrung-out will, of course, increase drying time.

2. Air flow restriction. Check ducts, lint traps, exhaust outdoor outlet. Check also for improper blower functioning, loose blower drive belt, worn out moving parts on blower, etc.

3. Cutout temperature may be too low. Make temperature check as given above. If cutout temperature is lower than minus tolerance given in manufacturer's literature, the cycling thermostat should be replaced, unless the range adjusting screw is accessible for field adjustment.

4. Low voltage (in electric dryers). Check voltage at power source and at the dryer terminals. If voltage drop is excessive (20 or more volts) replace branch line with next larger size wire. If voltage is low at power source, consult local utility.

Gas Pilot Flame Will Not Stay Lit

1. Check positioning of thermocouple joint in relation to pilot flame. One-half inch of tip of thermocouple should be buried in the flame, with the flame breaking around it. Adjust height of flame by turning pilot flame adjusting screw until flame burns blue without hissing noise.

2. Check circuitry from thermocouple to solenoid coil.

129

Gas Pilot Flame Will Not Light

1. Check gas supply and house gas valve as well as dryer main gas valve, and pilot-burner solenoid valve.
2. If glow coil is employed, check 24/2.5-volt circuit for breaks. Check visually for breaks in glow coil. Replace if necessary.

Gas Main Burner Will Not Light

1. Check main-burner solenoid valve and circuitry with test lamp for breaks or shorts in magnetic coil.
2. Check main-burner air shutter for clogging. Adjusting screw releases shutter so that it may be turned to admit more or less air until a clean-burning blue flame with a minimum of noise is achieved.

CHAPTER 5

RANGES

Electric and gas ranges have few moving parts and are therefore singularly free from servicing problems. However, some of the more recent models of electric ranges employ switches offering a number of heat settings between High and Simmer. These switches may occasionally require calibration and adjustment or replacement due to burnouts, etc.

TYPES OF GASES

There are three main types of gases used as fuel gases in ranges: manufactured, natural, and liquefied petroleum (LP). A fourth type, known as a "mixed" gas, is merely a mixture of manufactured and natural gases.

Manufactured gas is obtained as a by-product in the processing of coal. There are two chief types, coke oven gas and carbureted water gas. Coke oven gas is produced by "cooking" coal with external heat while at the same time denying it contact with air or oxygen. Carbureted water gas is produced by introducing live steam on a burning coal or coke bed. A compound is formed composed principally of hydrogen and carbon monoxide. This compound is then enriched with oil-produced gas. Manufactured gases are lowest in heat producing qualities, ranging from above 500 to 600 Btu per cubic foot.

Natural gases are obtained from the gas wells that are always present where oil is found deep within the earth. The chief ingredient of natural gas is methane, about 75% to 95% in volume. The other important ingredient is ethane, making up most of the remainder. Natural gas is a good heat producer, ranging from 950 to nearly 1,200 Btu per cubic foot.

Two liquefied petroleum gases are produced as a by-product of petroleum refining. One of these, butane, has a very high heat value—2,500 Btu per cubic foot. The other, propane, is rated at 1,500 Btu per cubic foot. Their special properties permit these gases to be stored and delivered in a liquid state under a moderate amount of pressure; hence the term "bottled gas." It is used mainly in rural areas not serviced by utility pipe lines.

Differences in characteristics require that appliances to be used with one of these three types of gases be altered with respect to the size of the orifice on burners. Distributor stocks of ranges will be equipped with orifices of the proper size for the type of gas being delivered in the area. In addition, a tag or some other means will be used to identify the type of gas for which the range was equipped.

In some cases, utility companies have switched from manufactured gas to natural gas, or vice versa. It is then the responsibility of the utility to make any necessary alterations.

Adjusting a Gas Flame

All gas burners are equipped with an air shutter which admits air in varying amounts to be mixed with the gas in burning (Fig. 5-1). To adjust the flame for maximum heat output, open the air supply until a soft blue flame is achieved. Gradually cut down the air supply until a yellow tip appears on the flame top. Now increase the air supply until the yellow tip just disappears. The flame should have a well defined, blue inner cone. Once the air shutter is properly adjusted, it should be locked in place with the set screw provided.

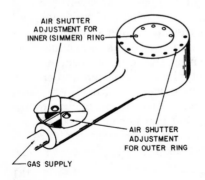

AIR SHUTTER
ADJUSTMENT FOR
INNER (SIMMER) RING

AIR SHUTTER
ADJUSTMENT
FOR OUTER RING

GAS SUPPLY

Fig. 5-1. Air-shutter adjustment of a gas burner.

Apart from the occasional need for gas flame adjustment, gas ranges require little maintenance except for cleaning the burner orifices.

THERMAL CONTROLS FOR GAS RANGES

Many gas ranges today make use of electrical components to control gas flow, thereby achieving automatic control of ovens and burners. In a typical oven temperature control system, three electrical components make up the system:

Electric Oven Thermostat—A standard electric range thermostat that simply turns the current on and off. Manual operation of the thermostat, by the oven control knob, closes the contacts; thermal action of the bulb, as the oven temperature is satisfied, opens the contacts.

Electric Gas Valve—This is a simple solenoid valve, actuated electrically. A gate opens and closes, allowing gas to flow to the oven burners or interrupting the flow.

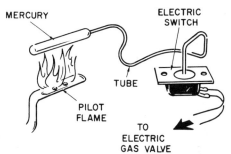

Fig. 5-2. Gas flame switch.

Flame Switch—Fig. 5-2 illustrates a safety device which assures that no gas can flow to the oven burners unless the pilot flame is lit. Once lit by the service man, it stays lit and does not interfere with the operation of the electric gas valve unless by inadvertence the pilot flame goes out.

The flame switch is designed around a slim tube of mercury positioned so that the tube is heated by the pilot flame. When the flame is on, the mercury in the tube expands, closing electrical contacts in the electric gas valve circuit, permitting the gas valve to open. When the pilot flame goes out, the mercury contacts open the electrical circuit. Further manual operation of the thermostat will have no effect on the electric gas valve, which stays shut off until the pilot flame is lit once again.

With the pilot flame lit, the automatically controlled gas-fired oven is ready for use. See Fig. 5-3. By selecting a tem-

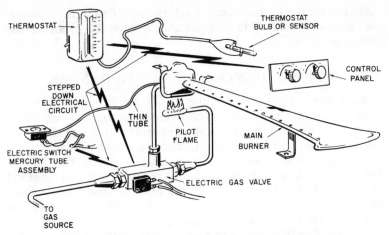

Fig. 5-3. Electrically controlled gas-fired range system.

perature on the oven thermostat, the customer closes a set of
contacts which complete the circuit to the electric gas valve.
Gas flows to the oven burners and is ignited by the pilot flame.
Most oven temperature control gas systems cycle the gas full
on and full off, with no attempt being made to restrict or
moderate the flow of gas to the oven burner. Cycling off and
on is accomplished by the bulb of a thermostat located in the
oven compartment and filled with a fluid. When the oven temperature rises, the fluid expands through a fine tube into a
bellows, which expands with heat and opens a set of electrical
contacts. This, in turn, interrupts the flow of electricity to
the electric gas valve and it shuts off, interrupting the flow
of gas to the oven burner. When the oven cools off (provided
the thermostat has not been turned to the off position, closing
the electrical circuit to the electric gas valve), gas is permitted to flow once again, and ignite the pilot flame in the oven.

A variation of the system described is the system used in
gas dryers described in Chapter 4. In this system, a thermocouple substitutes for the mercury tube, rendering it unnecessary to connect the range to an electrical power source. Instead of cycling full on and full off, as in the previous system
discussed, the burner may produce a by-pass flame that will
serve to maintain temperature in the oven once it has reached
the desired level.

By adding another component to the system, an electrically
actuated solenoid gas valve, it is possible to control the oven
remotely. The solenoid valve leads are attached to a clock
mechanism which opens the valve at a pre-set time and closes

it at a later preset time. Thus, the oven will light itself, achieve and maintain a preselected temperature, and then shut itself off. A further refinement adds an additional step in the thermostat operation by providing a period of a half hour or so before the expiration of cooking time during which the oven cools down to approximately 170° F. Since many of these sophisticated systems operate on low voltage, a transformer is generally introduced into the system, stepping the voltage down from 115 volts to as low as 11 volts. This, of course, permits the manufacturer to use components that are lighter and less expensive.

Calibrating a thermally controlled gas oven is accomplished exactly the same as for electric ovens. Calibration is nothing more than ensuring that the temperature reading on the dial of the thermostat control matches within a few degrees the actual temperature of the oven itself. Temperature checks should be made after the gas burner has cycled off and on at least two or three times after arriving at the desired temperature, to make sure heat has permeated all parts of the oven.

Thermally Controlled Top Burner

Many "automatic" gas ranges have at least one thermally controlled top burner, described as the type that will never cause food to burn. The control on this type of burner is handled by a sensor device which makes contact with the bottom of the cooking vessel. As the sensor approaches the temperature set by the customer on the thermostat dial, a bi-metal switch warps, seating a ball in the valve-seat of the gas valve. The burner shuts off, and the sensor cools down slightly as the food in the cooking vessel cools. The bi-metallic switch in the sensor returns to normal, sweeping the ball off the valve-seat and permitting gas to flow again.

The sensor cycles on and off rapidly until the preset temperature is reached. At that time it will cycle only to maintain the preset temperature. If food in the cooking vessel should dry out, which would normally cause the temperature in the vessel to soar well above the boiling point, scorching the food, the burner would remain off.

ELECTRIC RANGES

Electric ranges, like gas models, have two separate sets of heaters—the surface units and the oven unit or units. Ovens are generally equipped with two units; an overhead unit for Broil, and an oven floor unit that is used in conjunction with the upper unit for Bake. Surface units and oven units have separate control switches.

Until recently, most electric ranges employed both a 115-volt and a 230-volt circuit, used together in various combinations to achieve the different degrees of heat required for cooking. Now, however, most modern ranges use only 230-volt current controlled by a bimetal or bulb-type thermostatic switch which cycles the current on and off for shorter or longer periods to achieve the desired heat ranges.

Power Supply

Most modern electric ranges require 115/230-volt, three-wire, single-phase, 60-cycle alternating current (Fig. 5-4). Ranges are usually rated at approximately 60 amperes capacity, but fused at 50 amperes. While the maximum amperage of the range may exceed its fuse capacity, it is unlikely that all the range units will be turned on High at the same time, so fusing is set at approximately 80% of the full amperage rating of the range. The user should be instructed about this to avoid the nuisance of a blown fuse.

Electric ranges cannot be used on a 230-volt, two-wire, single-phase system, nor on a 230-volt, three wire, three-phase system. They cannot, of course, properly be operated on 115-volt, two-wire service because of voltage requirements.

Referring back to the ampere/wire size chart in Chapter 1, it can be seen that a 65-ampere capacity requires heavy No. 6 wires to carry the load of a high-wattage appliance such as the electric range.

An electric range is normally directly wired, meaning that no line cord is provided for plugging into an outlet. A heavy-duty, three-pronged, grounded wall outlet may be provided if local electrical codes permit. The method of connecting the range to the distribution box is shown in Fig. 5-5.

Surface Units

Surface units may be of two types—the older wire-coil type (Fig. 5-6), similar to a hot plate with the wire coils exposed, or the newer tubular unit (Fig. 5-7). In the latter, a wire coil is contained in a magnesium alloy tube and isolated (rather than insulated) from the tube by porcelain or composition spacers through which the wire coil is threaded. The wire coils are made from specially treated alloys selected for their resistance to intense heat.

The wattage, or heat-producing capacity, of the surface unit is directly related to the number and size of the wire coils,

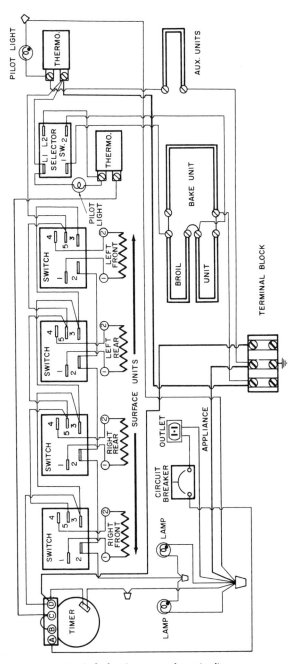

Fig. 5-4. Typical electric range schematic diagram.

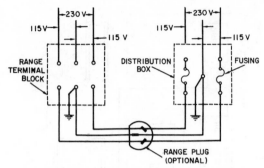

Fig. 5-5. Method used in connecting the range to house wiring.

which set up an ohmic resistance to the electrical current. In most ranges there are three surface units of approximately 1250 watts each, and one larger unit of approximately 2000 or 2100 watts.

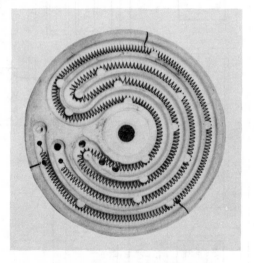

Fig. 5-6. "Hot-plate" type of surface unit.

Surface Unit Temperature Control Switches

As mentioned before, a variation in the amount of heat produced by a unit may be achieved in one of two ways: the 115/230-volt coils controlled by a switch whose settings may be changed to apply 115 or 230 volts, arranging the coils in series or in parallel. The other method uses 230 volts only in conjunction with an infinite heat switch, which will be examined later.

Fig. 5-7. Tubular surface unit.

Fig. 5-8 shows a three-heat switch in a typical arrangement. Note that the two heating elements, an inner and outer coil, offer differing ohmic resistance to the current, making the inner coil a hotter element than the outer coil. To achieve high heat, 115 volts are applied to both the elements in parallel. For medium heat, only the inner coil is energized. For low heat, the switch directs 115 volts across both elements connected in series, resulting in greatly lowered wattage.

Fig. 5-9 illustrates the method employed for a seven-position switch. At High heat, both elements are connected in parallel to 230 volts. At the Medium High position, 230 volts is applied to the inner coil. Medium position connects the outer coil with 230 volts. In the Medium Low position, both

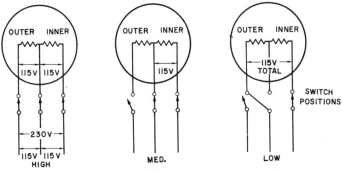

Fig. 5-8. Three-setting switch, showing arrangement of contacts at each switch setting.

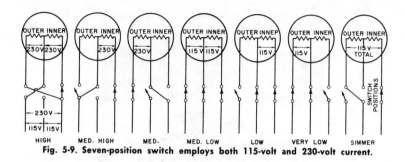

Fig. 5-9. Seven-position switch employs both 115-volt and 230-volt current.

elements are connected in parallel to 115 volts. Low position connects the inner coil to 115 volts; on Very Low, 115 volts is applied to the outer coil; and Simmer applies a 115-volt current across both elements in series.

The more recent method of achieving variation in heat for surface units is by means of a bimetal switch, similar in principle to a thermostat. However, instead of being acted on by external heat, its own internal heat causes it to cycle on and off. Inside the switch (Fig. 5-10), bimetal strip A has an electrical contact at one end, the other end being anchored in the body of the switch. As current passes through the bimetal strip, it tends to curl up and away from the contact at the end of another metal strip, B. The latter is spring-loaded so that it presses against a spiral cam surface actuated by a switch knob.

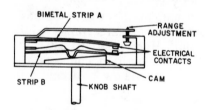

Fig. 5-10. Bimetal surface unit infinite heat switch.

Another set of contacts is opened manually whenever the knob is turned to Off.

When the knob is rotated 45° clockwise, a sharp incline on the cam surface drives metal strip B up tightly against the bimetal strip, making a firm contact. In the High position, the bimetal strip cannot curl sufficiently to break the contact, with the result that the surface unit is continuously on at the High position. As the knob is rotated clockwise, the force of the spring pressing strip B against bimetal strip A is lessened. As electrical current flows through bimetal strip A, it warms up and curls away from its contact with strip B. However, since

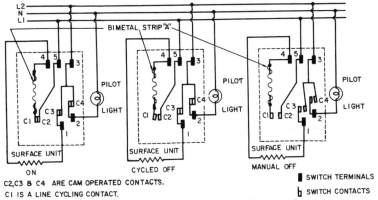

C2, C3 & C4 ARE CAM OPERATED CONTACTS.
C1 IS A LINE CYCLING CONTACT.

Fig. 5-11. Schematic diagram of the infinite heat switch.

the cam surface is close to its highest point, the bimetal strip will not break contact until a relatively long period has elapsed.

The more the knob is turned clockwise (toward Low) the shorter these On periods will be until, at the Simmer position, the surface unit will cycle on for only about 20 to 60 seconds out of every 10-minute period.

Fig. 5-11 shows a schematic of the infinite heat switch. Note the difference between "cycled off" (by the action of the bimetal strip) and "manual off" (by the action of the knob).

Surface unit infinite heat switches may be calibrated for proper heat input. First, set a flat-bottomed sauce pan partially filled with water on the unit to be checked. Turn the control knob to Low Boil, if such a setting exists, or to a point just below High. The water should come to a definite boil within a reasonable length of time, but it should not attain a vigorous, rolling boil.

Change the setting by removing the control knob to uncover a set screw. The screw may be recessed so that it can be reached only through a hole in the body of the switch. If the water did not attain a definite boil in the test, increase the temperature by turning the set screw counterclockwise. If the boil was too vigorous, decrease the temperature by turning the set screw clockwise. If changing the setting of the screw does not affect the temperature, the switch is defective and should be replaced.

Oven Units

As mentioned previously, modern electric ranges employ two tubular oven units, a broil unit at the top of the oven and a bake unit at the bottom. The broil unit is made up of two coils, with a combined wattage of about 3000 watts. The bake unit is a single coil with approximately 2500 watts rating. When baking, the bake unit should glow red, and the broil unit should get hot, but not red. When the selector switch is set at Broil, the broil unit should glow red too.

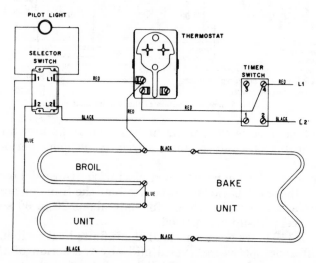

Fig. 5-12. Wiring diagram showing the selector switch and the oven control thermostat.

In addition to the main oven, some ranges feature a second, smaller, oven which is called by a variety of trade names. It may have a smaller tubular unit, rated at about 1500 watts, and is used for preparing small, quick meals. Some ranges feature a second, separate, oven of equal size which permits baking and roasting at the same time.

Adjustment of oven temperature requires two controls—a selector switch and a thermostat (Fig. 5-12). The selector switch generally has three positions, Bake, Broil and Off. The Bake position of the switch places the two coils of the broil unit in series, with resulting low wattage across the coils. In this position, the bake unit will glow red, but the broil unit will not. In the Broil position, the switch places the two coils of the broil unit in parallel, with resulting high wattage, causing the unit to glow red.

The thermostat (Fig. 5-13) is marked off in degrees of temperature. It causes both units to cycle off when the proper temperature setting is reached, and cycle on again when the

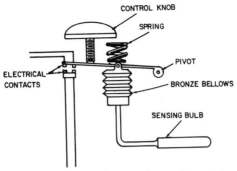

Fig. 5-13. Pictorial diagram of oven thermostat.

temperature falls below a lower limit that has been pre-determined.

Ovens generally employ a bulb and bellows-type thermostat, filled with a liquid. As the bulb senses more heat, the liquid expands slightly, pushing open a bronze collapsible bellows which works against the force of a spring to open a pair of electrical contacts. With the source of heat eliminated, the liquid contracts, and the bellows tends to collapse under the force of the spring until the contacts are remade.

Timers

Timers may be provided for the oven unit only, or they may control each of the surface units as well. One such arrangement is shown schematically in Fig. 5-4. The timer is powered by a synchronous motor. It may also incorporate a clock as part of the assembly.

The timer assembly consists of a set of cam wheels, very much the same as the timer found on automatic washing machines. A series of terminals opens or closes the appropriate circuits to surface units, ovens or appliance outlets, as selected by the user.

Spring-powered timers may also be found on earlier models of electric ranges. These are simply a clock mechanism which is wound and set at the same time by the control knob. When the winding runs out, a mechanical train forces open a pair of electrical contacts to open the circuit.

Electric ranges may be equipped with a thermostat that provides a cooled-down period just before the expiration of an automatically preset cooking time. This would work in the same manner as the system described for gas ranges, except, of course, electrical switches would be actuated instead of gas solenoid valves.

Circuit Breakers

Ranges rated at 60 amperes and fused at the branch line with only 50-ampere fuses require an additional fusing arrangement at the range to eliminate the nuisance of blown branch line fuses caused by accidental or inadvertent turning of all the units on High. This is usually accomplished by a circuit breaker, generally located on the control panel for easy access.

When the range wattage consumption exceeds the high limit set by the circuit breaker, threatening to blow the branch line fuse, the circuit breaker will snap open the contacts, shutting off all power to the range. The user should have been instructed to turn off all the units and reset the button on the circuit breaker. However, if the overload condition that caused the circuit breaker to open still persists, the breaker will not reset in the closed position.

Circuit breakers, as mentioned before, are energized when the force of a magnetic field created by a current exceeds the holding power of a spring-loaded mechanism. See Fig. 5-4 for wiring details.

Appliance Outlets

Convenient outlets are incorporated in most electrical ranges, supplying 115-volt current for the operation of small appliances on or near the range (Fig. 5-4).

Accessories

Various other features, such as an electrically driven oven spit, glass doors, and deep-well cookers are offered by range manufacturers. These are generally simple devices, easily traced through the wiring harness of the 115-volt circuit.

PERFORMANCE CHECKS

Probably the greatest single complaint a technician will be confronted with in servicing electric ranges is the calibration of the oven. Most oven thermostats are equipped with a range set screw which may be adjusted in the field. Calibration is accomplished by using a thermocouple which may be externally mounted and read so that it is unnecessary to open the oven door to read the temperature. (An appliance tester usually incorporates a thermocouple dial for reading temperatures.) Place the sensing end of the thermocouple on a rack at or near the center of the oven. Thread the lead wire through the bottom or hinged side of the door, and connect the plug into the receptacle on the appliance tester.

Close the oven door and set the temperature control at 400°F. Allow the oven units to cycle off and on at least twice before taking a reading. This is to allow for overshooting in temperature as the oven liner absorbs heat.

The oven temperature should rise a few degrees above the setting before cutting out, and drop a few degrees below the setting before cutting in again. A maximum allowable variation would be about 25°F above or below the 400°F setting of the dial. Anything greater than this would cause serious miscalculation in baking or roasting, and would indicate that adjustment or replacement of the thermostat is required.

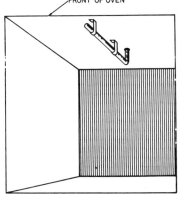

Fig. 5-14. Location of sensing bulb of thermostat in typical oven.

It is sometimes possible to make a quick adjustment simply by relocating the control knob on its shaft so that the indicator points lower or higher than the previous setting. If this does not accomplish the desired result, it will be necessary to disassemble the control panel to gain access to the thermostat. Most thermostats are provided with a range adjusting screw, with the proper direction for increasing and decreasing temperature marked by an arrow. Generally, one quarter turn counterclockwise *raises* the temperature 25°F.; the same turn clockwise *lowers* the temperature 25°F. In making this adjustment, the *spread*, or differential between the high and low limits of the thermostat, should not be disturbed. In most thermostats, the differential setting is sealed at the factory so that it cannot be changed.

An excessive differential setting is cause for replacement of the entire thermostat assembly. Fig. 5-14 shows the arrangement of the thermostat sensing bulb in the oven.

SURFACE UNIT CHECK

With the switch on High, make a voltage check at the surface unit terminals with a voltmeter or a neon test light. If the neon light glows brightly or if the voltmeter reads 230 to 240 volts, the surface unit is defective and should be replaced. If no voltage is recorded, a check of the switch is indicated. Check for voltage across the terminals indicated in the manufacturer's literature. If the proper voltage is read, the wiring between the switch and the surface unit is probably satisfactory. If no reading is obtained, the switch may be defective.

CHAPTER 6

DISHWASHERS

The principle of operation of a dishwasher is simple and direct: hot water and detergent, driven at high speed, are sprayed over dirty dishes by a motor-driven impeller or by a rotating spray arm from which the water emerges. After several rinses and drains the same impeller wafts air warmed by a heating element over the dishes to dry them.

Dishwashers are of several kinds, mostly having to do with mounting and location in the kitchen. The portable dishwasher (Fig. 6-1) may be wheeled over to the dinner table, where the dishes are scraped and loaded through a door in the top. The dishwasher is then wheeled back to its normal location at or near the sink, water connections are made, the line cord is plugged into an outlet and the machine turned on.

The undercounter model (Fig. 6-2) is designed to fit just under a standard-height countertop next to the sink. Water and electrical connections are permanent, in most models the dishwasher is directly wired to the distribution box. Some undercounter models have a bottom-hinged door which opens in the same manner as a range oven door. Trays slide out to accept the dishes or the entire tub rolls out for top loading.

Dishwashers are also available as combination sinks (Fig. 6-3) which incorporate a garbage disposer.

DISHWASHER FUNCTIONING

With respect to functioning, there are two general systems in popular use. One is the impeller dishwasher, in which a motor-driven impeller blade splatters water in all directions inside the tub. The other is the spray-arm dishwasher, in which water is recirculated by a separate pump, emerging from

Fig. 6-1. Portable dishwasher.

the nozzles of the spray arm, which rotates by recoil, much the same as a lawn sprinkler.

Thus, in both types the washing of the dishes is accomplished by a combination of the mechanical force of the water striking and dislodging soil, and the dissolving action of the hot, sudsy water on grease and other foreign matter.

Fig. 6-4 depicts the functioning of a typical impeller-type dishwasher. The dishes are arranged in the tub so that they

Fig. 6-2. Undercounter dishwasher.

will drain properly and not trap water. The tub is closed and the interlocking door switch is turned on. The tub cannot be opened in any dishwasher unless this switch is turned off first, to prevent accidental water spillage into the room. Now the timer switch is advanced to Start and the machine turns on.

A timer motor, similar to the type found in automatic washers, advances a series of cams, whose raised surfaces open and close circuits in order in the course of their slow rotation. The first cam closes a circuit to a solenoid-operated water inlet valve. Water for the dishwasher is connected to the hot-water pipe only—there is no mixing or selection of hot, warm, or cold, as in a clothes washer. Recommended water temperature, received directly from the home hot water heater, is 140°F to 160°F. Any water temperature lower than 140°F will result in dishes that are not only filmy and spotted, but less germ-free than they would be at the proper temperature.

The inlet valve operates as a timed fill, the amount of flow being governed by a flow washer. A typical fill cycle lasts about 60 seconds, admits about 12 pints of water, flowing at a rate of about 1½ gallons per minute. Some dishwashers provide a pressure switch, similar to the pressure fill switch found in automatic washers. However, the function of the pressure switch in a dishwasher is to shut off the water *in the event* the proper water level is reached before the timer motor shuts off the water inlet valve; this is due to the variations in water flow rate. Thus, the pressure switch in a dishwasher is a water-level safety device.

When the user advances the timer switch, water enters the tub through the water-inlet valve, as described. At the same time, the main motor circuit closes and the impeller begins to rotate at a motor speed of about 1,700 rpm. As water reaches the impeller, it is driven forcefully against the dirty dishes,

UNIT

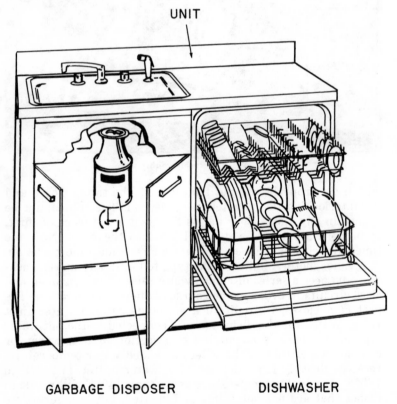

GARBAGE DISPOSER   DISHWASHER

Fig. 6-3. A typical combination sink, dishwasher, and garbage disposer.

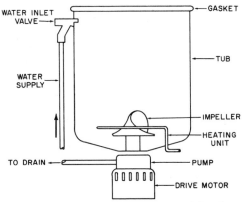

Fig. 6-4. Functioning of impeller-type dishwasher.

to "scrub rinse" them and soften the soil in preparation for washing.

The timer cams having advanced after a short period, the circuit to the solenoid valve is opened and water flow into the tub is stopped. The impeller continues to rotate for a short time, until the timer cams advance and the circuit to the main motor is opened. After a brief pause, the motor circuit is closed again, but this time in reverse.

Most dishwashers employ a shaded-pole, variable speed, reversible motor for this purpose (Chapter 10).

The reverse rotation of the motor causes the drain pump to function. A system of valves and the arrangement of the interior-pump impeller blades cause the pump to idle in one direction, and pump water in the other direction. Water is pumped directly into the sink drain.

The drain cycle is also a timed cycle, allowing ample time for the dishwasher tub to be drained. During draining, the main motor impeller is mechanically disconnected and does not move throughout this period.

After the first rinse cycle, some dishwashers provide a second rinse. Now follows a period of washing, lasting from 5 to 7 minutes.

Water is admitted to the tub for the wash cycle in the same manner as for a rinse. After a short period during which the impeller drives water against the dishes, a cam on the shaft of the timer motor dislodges a detent lever, and the detergent cup is upended by the force of a spring, spilling dry detergent into the tub. The detergent causes low sudsing, and the hot, sudsy solution washes away the presoftened dirt and emulsifies greasy films and stains.

151

When the washing period has elapsed, the timer cam advances and draining takes place. This is followed by at least two rinses, each followed by a drain period. After the final rinse, the main motor impeller is driven at high speed, becoming a fan that is capable of delivering a relatively large volume of air. At the same time, a circuit to the heating element located in the bottom of the tub is energized. Heating elements are rated at from 600 to 1,000 watts and are used to assist in the drying process. Air warmed by the heating element is circulated throughout the tub by the main motor impeller. Venting is accomplished by water-baffling holes in the top gasket, which lead steam out of the interior of the tub. The drain pump would also assist in this function in those dishwashers in which it operates during the warming and drying period. After a period of drying, lasting about 25 minutes, the timer advances and all circuits are opened.

Fig. 6-5 is a diagram of a spray-arm circulating dishwasher. The main differences between this type and the impeller type are: (1) a separate motor for each of two pumps, a recirculating pump and a drain pump; and (2) the spray arm which replaces the main motor impeller.

In the spray-arm dishwasher, water is admitted in the same manner as the impeller type, through a solenoid-operated water inlet valve. Water runs down into a sump, passing through a filter screen in its passage. From the sump, it is forced under pressure into the spray arm by the recirculating pump. The nozzles on the spray arm are slanted at an angle so that the recoil action of the water ejected from the nozzles drives the spray arm shaft to rotate at high speed. Thus, water

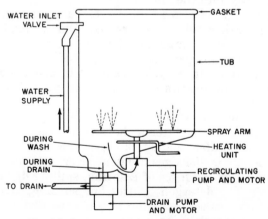

Fig. 6-5. Spray-arm circulating-pump dishwasher.

is sprayed into every angle and crevice formed by the dishes on the racks.

Fig. 6-6 shows how a spray-arm dishwasher filters small particles out of the wash water before they are permitted to reach the recirculating pump and clog the relatively small nozzle openings of the spray-arm shaft. The circulating action of the water causes particles to gravitate toward the center of the slope formed by the tub. Both coarse and fine particles roll down the slope and onto a fine screen, with a cone-shaped hole

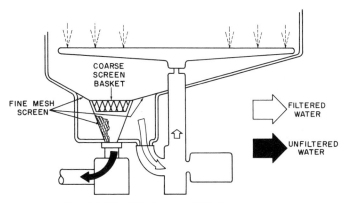

Fig. 6-6. Pictorial diagram of filtering system.

in its center. Placed in the hole is a coarse-screen basket, which traps and holds the particles too large to be admitted into the drain pump. Smaller particles pass through the basket and are held temporarily inside the cone-shaped portion of the fine-mesh filter screen, where they are prevented from entering the inlet to the recirculating pump. Filtered water now passes through the fine-mesh screen, where it is admitted to the recirculating pump and on to the spray arm.

When draining occurs, all the smaller particles held temporarily in the cone-shaped filter pass down into the drain pump and out the drain. The larger particles trapped by the coarse screen basket are lifted out with the basket, which should be emptied after each use or as necessary.

ELECTRICAL SYSTEM

Dishwashers are powered by a 115-volt, three-wire, single-phase, alternating current, rated at from 12 to 15 amperes. Because of the relatively high power consumption of a dishwasher at full load, it should be wired to its own branch circuit, except

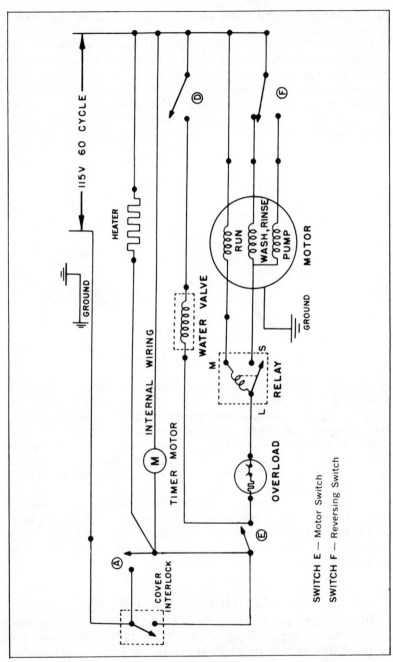

Fig. 6-7. Schematic wiring diagram for impeller-type dishwasher.

154

for portable dishwashers.

Fig. 6-7 shows a typical schematic wiring diagram for an impeller-type dishwasher. The wash-timer sequence chart in Fig. 6-8 relates to the machine represented in the wiring diagram and is similar to the automatic clothes-washer sequence chart seen in Chapter 3. Note that in this machine the heater cycles on during the wash period to aid in heating the water. Note also that it is used at two different wattage settings, one for washing and the other for drying. In this machine the heater is turned off 11 timer increments before shut-off to allow the dishes to cool down for easier handling.

Fig. 6-9 shows a typical schematic diagram for the spray-arm type dishwasher in which separate circuits are provided

Table 6-1. Timer Circuit Function

MACHINE FUNCTION		TIMER INCREMENT	ACTIVE CIRCUITS			
OFF		0-1				
1st PRERINSE	DRAIN	2	1 2	4		
	FILL	3	1	3 4 5		
	RINSE	4-5	1	4 5	6	
	DRAIN	6	1 2	4 5		
PREWASH	FILL	7	1	3 4 5		
	WASH	8-10	1	4 5	6	
	DRAIN	11	1 2	4 5		
2nd PRERINSE	FILL	12	1	3 4 5		
	RINSE	13-15	1	4 5	6	
	DRAIN	16	1 2	4		
WASH	FILL	17	1	3 4		
	WASH	18-30	1	4 5	6	
	DRAIN	31	1 2	4 5		
1st RINSE	FILL	32	1	3 4 5		
	RINSE	33-34	1	4 5	6	
	DRAIN	35	1 2	4 5		
2nd RINSE	FILL	36	1	3 4 5		
	RINSE	37-41	1	4 5	6	
	DRAIN	42	1 2	4 5		
DRY	DRY	43-58	1	4	6	
	DRAIN	59	1 2	4	6	
	DRY	60	1	4	6	

NOTE: EACH TIMER INCREMENT—45 SECONDS.

NOTE: ACTIVE CIRCUITS COLUMN REFERS TO ENCIRCLED NUMBERS ON DIAGRAM.

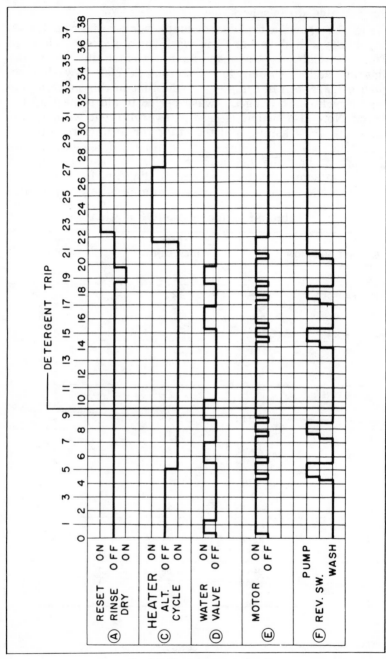

Fig. 6-8. Timer sequence chart.

for the circulating-pump motor and the drain-pump motor. Note the numbered circuits in this diagram, which are shown in the last column of the sequence chart, Table 6-1. This latter shows timer sequence in a different manner, but it provides essentially the same information as that shown in Fig. 6-8.

Timer

In timers used in dishwashers, a synchronous motor drives a mechanical train, which, in turn, drives a cam wheel (or a series of cam wheels). The cam advances in increments of time, usually about 45 seconds in duration. Normally, the timer motor operates continuously throughout the cycle of operation.

In some models the timer is equipped with a master line switch wired in series. Its purpose is to interrupt the circuit whenever the timer dial is being reset, particularly in those machines which offer a selection of short and long cycles of operation.

Water-Inlet Valve

Fig. 6-10 shows a typical water-inlet valve operated by a solenoid, such as those seen in automatic clothes washers. When using a timed fill, and without any positive means of regulating water level, it is important to regulate the flow rate of the incoming water. (Actually, in impeller-type dishwashers, water level is a fiction. The water in the tub never gets a chance to find a level, being always in motion under the force of the impeller. A few impeller-driven models provide a sump for determining water levels, but most dishwashers of the impeller type do not.)

Flow rate is accomplished by the flow washer, which flexes under the pressure of the water. The greater the pressure, the more the washer flexes, presenting a smaller opening for the passage of the water. Thus, even under varying water-pressure conditions (which may vary from 15 to over 100 psi), the flow washer affords a uniform rate of flow. In addition, flow washers of greater or less flow rate may be substituted in the inlet valve for different conditions. Flow washers may permit a flow rate ranging from 1 to 2 gallons per minute.

In the drawing (Fig. 6-10) the solenoid plunger is in the closed position. Pressure of the water at B is the same as water pressure in the house lines. A bleed hole in the diaphragm washer permits the water pressures at B and C to equalize each other. But the area of diaphragm in contact with the water pressure at C is greater than the area at B, forcing the dia-

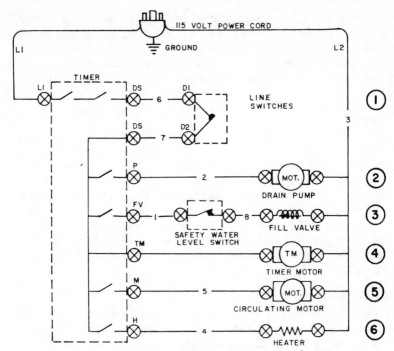

Fig. 6-9. Schematic wiring diagram for spray-arm dishwasher.

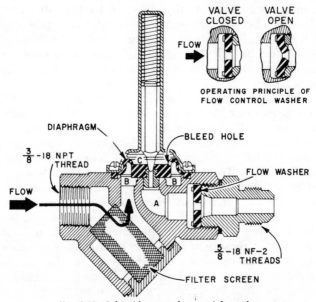

Fig. 6-10. Solenoid-operated water-inlet valve.

phragm downward to seat firmly on the valve seat. Water pressure at A is atmospheric pressure, the opening of the inlet valve being exposed to the air in the tub.

When the solenoid plunger is withdrawn from the hole in the center of the diaphragm washer, water pressure at C pushes the diaphragm away from its seat in the valve and water passes through the valve, governed by the flow washer, and into the dishwasher tub.

Most water-inlet valves are equipped with fine-mesh filters to screen out impurities.

Heaters

Dishwasher heaters are of tubular construction (Fig. 6-11), similar to the tubular surface and oven-range units described in Chapter 5. In some dishwashers they serve the dual purpose of supplying auxiliary heat for the wash and rinse water and

Fig. 6-11. Tubular heating element used in dishwashers.

as a heat source in the drying cycle. They may be anywhere from 600 to 1,000 watts. The wire coil is completely enclosed in a magnesium alloy tube and held from contact with the tubing by porcelain or other nonconducting spacers. Rubber or neoprene washers make a waterproof seal at the two points of entry of the heater element in the tub.

Pressure Switch

A typical pressure switch, Fig. 6-12, is actuated by a diaphragm located in the bottom of a sump, or well, in the tub. It consists of a single-pole, double-throw switch with two sets of electrical contacts. A normally closed set of contacts is in series with the solenoids of the water-inlet valve. If the timed fill should result in an overflow above the normal water level, the normally closed contacts will open the circuit to the solenoid. At the same time, a pair of normally open contacts leading to the drain pump will close, and the pump will operate to drain off any excess water from the tub. When the pressure switch is satisfied as the water level recedes, the circuit to the drain pump assumes its normally open position, draining stops and the dishwashing cycle proceeds.

MECHANICAL SYSTEM

The few purely mechanical parts of a dishwasher, unlike an automatic clothes washer, result in an appliance that is remarkably service-free, considering all the functions it performs. Following is a description of the main mechanical assemblies in a typical dishwasher.

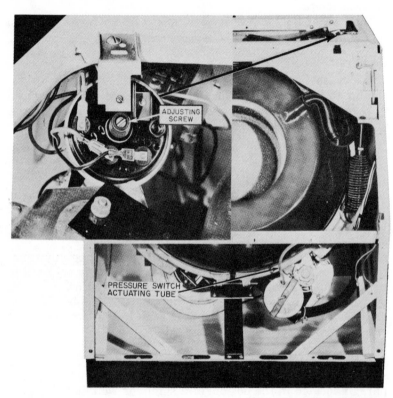

Courtesy Westinghouse Electric Corp.

Fig. 6-12. Pressure switch acts as water level safety switch.

Pumps

Dishwashers, whether of the impeller type or the spray-arm type, utilize pumps mounted directly on the drive motor shaft, with no gear train or drive belts as found in automatic clothes washers. However, the interior arrangement (Fig. 6-13) of the pump is similar to that found in the washer drain pump, with a series of flapper valves controlling whether the pump should drain or idle.

In the reversible motor dishwasher, when the motor is turning in a clockwise direction (looking toward the motor), washing is taking place at a rate of three or more gallons per minute. In the counterclockwise direction, pumping is taking place. In some models, the main motor impeller stops during drain; in others, the impeller turns, but because of the shape of the vanes, has little or no effect on the water in the tub.

Detergent Cup Mechanism

These mechanisms may take many forms in different makes, but the principle is similar in each. At a given point in the cycle, a trigger mechanism is tripped and the cup is overturned, spilling the detergent into the wash water.

Fig. 6-13. Interior of dishwasher drain pump.

A typical mechanism is shown in Fig. 6-14. The turning of the timer shaft, making one complete revolution during the entire cycle, turns a cam with it. When detergent is loaded into the machine, the cup is turned upright manually, against the force of a spring. A plunger engages with the cup, preventing it from overturning. The other end of this plunger is pressed against the face of the cam wheel on the timer shaft.

When the cam wheel rotates to a point where the cam surface makes a sudden drop, the plunger is forced by its own spring down into the lower surface of the cam wheel. At the other end, the plunger disengages from the cup, which snaps into the overturned position, spilling the contents.

A lid is provided on detergent cups to keep the detergent dry until it is ready to be added to the water. If the detergent becomes damp in the cup, it may pack down and fail to dispense properly. Some means of opening the lid is also usually provided so that wash water can penetrate into the interior of the cup after it is overturned to wash it clean.

Other detergent cup mechanisms may employ electromagnets to initiate triggering, although most of these would still depend on the force of springs to accomplish the actual overturning of the cup.

Some dishwashers employ two dispensing cups, one for the regular wash detergent and another for a rinse conditioner.

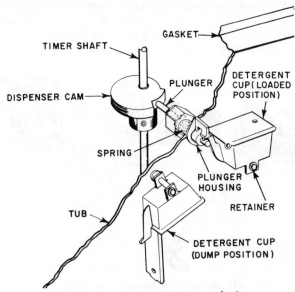

Fig. 6-14. Detergent-cup tripping mechanism.

PERFORMANCE CHECKS

As in all electrical appliances, voltage, wattage and amperage checks will reveal not only electrical faults, but mechanical faults as well. In a dishwasher, wattage checks will reveal faults in the impeller or spray-arm mechanical system and the internal-pump mechanism. For a full description of electrical performance checks which apply as well to the dishwasher see Chapter 3.

By comparing timer performance with standards published by the manufacturers, it is possible to detect other failures. Check the duration of timer increments for the number of seconds between the audible clicks of the timer as it advances. Also check the length of time of each cycle—rinse, wash, and dry.

INSTALLATION

Dishwashers may be installed in water systems having 15 to 120 psi. Anything less than 15 psi would result in inadequate fill and poor washing results. Pressures above 120 psi require the installation of a pressure-reducing valve ahead of the regular water-inlet valve. Water temperature should not be below 140°F for optimum washing results.

Permanent installations such as undercounter dishwashers should have a cut-off valve installed in the hot water line just preceding the water inlet valve, for convenience in servicing. The drain line is led directly into the line just above the sink

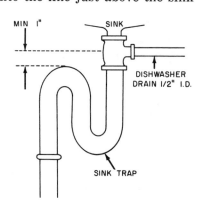

Fig. 6-15. Method of installing drain line into sink drain.

trap (Fig. 6-15). Water supply lines should be ⅜-inch I.D. copper tubing; the drain line should be ½-inch I.D. copper tubing.

Fusing and wiring should be of 15 amperes capacity (No. 14 wire). If a garbage disposer is used on the same line, fusing and wiring should be increased to 20 amperes (No. 12 wire). Grounding should be as provided by the manufacturer, or a separate ground wire should be installed between the grounding terminal on the dishwasher terminal box and a cold water pipe. Be sure that wiring to the dishwasher is confined to a space on the rear wall as specified in the installation instructions, to prevent interference with the suspension or roll-out mechanism.

WASHING COMPLAINTS

It is important that the user understand the need for proper racking of dishes and cups. These should be positioned so that no pools of water will form. Some cups and glasses have depressed centers and when turned upside down will collect a few drops of water that will not evaporate in the time allowed for drying. This is a condition that can be alleviated to some extent by slanting the items in the racks.

Hard water has a substantial effect on washability. A mineral coating on dishes and glassware is not only unsightly, but it slows the drying time considerably. The type of detergent used will greatly help in correcting this condition. Only detergent made especially for dishwashers should be used. In some areas, a rinse conditioner or a mechanical water softener provides the only effective solution.

Drying will be considerably slowed down if the water entering the dishwasher is not at the recommended minimum temperature.

Spotting of dishes and glassware can also be caused by improper water level, improper racking, and low water temperature.

To remove the accumulated film caused by spotting, the following procedure is recommended by manufacturers:

First, run the machine through a complete cycle with a regular load. Be certain to remove any silverware, pots and pans, and plastic utensils at this point, leaving only china and glassware. Turn the timer dial to Wash and allow the cycle to proceed until fill is accomplished. Stop the machine. Now mix about half to three-quarters of a cup of regular household bleach in several parts of water in a container. Place the container upright on a bottom rack (this dispenses the contents gradually). Let the Wash cycle continue until drain is accomplished. Stop the machine.

Empty the container in the sink and place about two cups of vinegar in it, replacing the container on the bottom rack. Run the machine through the wash cycle again, this time letting it continue to the end of the drying period.

The bleach/vinegar treatment will remove any spots or films that have formed. If necessary, this treatment can be repeated periodically.

TROUBLESHOOTING GUIDE

Following are the symptoms and probable causes of failure to be found in typical dishwashers.

Will Not Operate

1. Blown fuse due to overloaded circuit or short to ground. Replace fuse, but not before checking to determine if an

overload does exist or if a short is present. Replacing the fuse does not correct the condition. If the replacement fuse blows immediately on the start of the machine, look for overload conditions, shorts in the wiring harness, terminal box, timer, water-inlet valve solenoid and main motor. If fuse blows during cycling, check for shorts or mechanical binding in the various pump and impeller mechanisms.

2. Open circuit between terminal junction box and timer motor, or failure of door switch. Check continuity with test lamp at house wiring junction, power line to dishwasher, door switch or lid latch switch.
3. Defective timer switch (if provided). Check continuity with test lamp at appropriate terminals, being sure that timer dial is turned to the cycle marked On.
4. Defective timer motor. Check for loose connections, wrong leads to terminals, continuity to motor terminals, or jamming of timer mechanism.

Operates Independently of Timer Knob Position

1. If one of the electrical components has shorted out to ground, and the polarity of the dishwasher wiring has been reversed, the dishwasher will continue to operate, but not under the control of the timer lid latch switch, or door handle. Disconnect the dishwasher at the fuse box and correct the reversed polarity by installing the proper color wire on the color coded terminals at the junction box. *Correct the ground condition.*

Continues to Operate When Door is Opened

1. Faulty door switch. Check continuity, repair or replace door switch.

Part of Cycle Omitted or Shortened

1. Damaged timer assembly. Field repair or adjustment of timer assemblies is not usually feasible. Replace timer assembly.
2. Circuit not completed to proper timer terminal due to a broken wire or lead. Use ohmmeter to check continuity, following manufacturer's wiring diagram for color-coded wire.
3. The dishwasher may also perform part of the cycle at the incorrect time, due to crossing of the wires at the terminals of the timer. Check against manufacturer's wiring diagram.

Motor Will Not Run

1. If a hum is present, look for an obstruction on the impeller.
2. The automatic overload protector may have operated. Allow a few minutes for the protector to cool down, then try again. Check for low line voltage, binding in the motor or pump mechanism, or binding of impeller or spray-arm shaft.
3. Defective timer switch (see preceding). Also look for loose connections, broken wires, etc.
4. Defective motor. Check motor terminals with voltmeter. If reading is normal, and no binding exists, motor probably should be replaced.

Electric Shocks at Cabinet

1. Components or wires shorting or leaking current to structural parts of dishwasher. Check the ground lead for proper connection. Use the ohmmeter to check for shorts or excessive leakage.
2. If dishwasher transmits an electric shock when the timer is turned Off, a change in the polarity of the dishwasher wiring is indicated.

Water Will Not Shut Off

1. Water inlet valve stuck open. Disassemble and clean the valve, checking the solenoid movement.
2. Bleed hole in diaphragm washer of water inlet valve clogged. Disassemble and free hole.
3. Timer switch jammed in closed position. Replace switch.

Water Will Not Enter

1. Broken wire to water inlet valve solenoid. Check also for loose connection. Make continuity test with test lamp or visual inspection.
2. Check also for defective timer switch, solenoid coil or pressure switch. Other causes might be traced to crimped water inlet hose, low water pressure, a clogged screen in the water inlet valve or a flow washer installed backwards.

Water Leaks

1. Defective or worn door gasket, or improper loading causing unseating of cover panel on door gasket. Make visual inspection.

2. Defective drain pump or worn hoses. Make visual inspection for signs of leakage. Replace pump housing gasket, neoprene seals around entrance of heating elements, etc.
3. Too much water in tub. Check pressure switch and replace if necessary. Adjustment in the field is not usually feasible.

Dishes Do Not Dry

1. Drain pump faulty or inoperative. Listen for sounds of drain at sink drain. Gurgling should stop and drain pump continue to operate for a time before a new cycle starts. If gurgling continues right up to the new cycle, drain pump is not evacuating tub completely.
2. Water not hot enough. Check for temperature of at least 140°F at the tap.
3. Heating element disconnected. Check for loose or broken wires leading to element.
4. Heating element defective. Check for continuity across heating element contacts with wires removed; if no current, replace element.

Abnormal Noises

1. Spray arm or impeller striking objects. Check clearances and look for small items (silverware, etc.) which may have fallen through protective screen.
2. Machine not level or solidly mounted. Check installation and shim up any loose fitting cabinet or structural components.

CHAPTER 7

GARBAGE
DISPOSERS

Garbage disposers are attached to the kitchen sink drain and dispose of garbage by grinding or shredding it into small pieces, which are then washed down the drain by a continuing flow of cold water. As you can imagine, disposers are ruggedly constructed, yet have surprisingly few moving parts. Once installed, a disposer should be relatively trouble-free for years.

The cross-section view of the disposer (Fig. 7-1) is almost self-explanatory. Food waste enters the unit through the sink drain and the cover is placed in the sink drain hole. The user turns on the cold water tap to a moderate flow. In some models, a turn of the cover starts the shredding process—in others, a wall switch is actuated.

Waste reaches the bottom of the shredding compartment, where it comes in contact with a whirling impeller (1,700 rpm). There, centrifugal force, acting on the waste, squeezes it against vertical teeth or slots in a stationary shredder ring. A vane on the impeller chops off the waste at the intersection of the vane and teeth. As the process continues, waste is ground up into particles small enough to pass through the teeth, aided by the water flow, into a lower evacuation chamber.

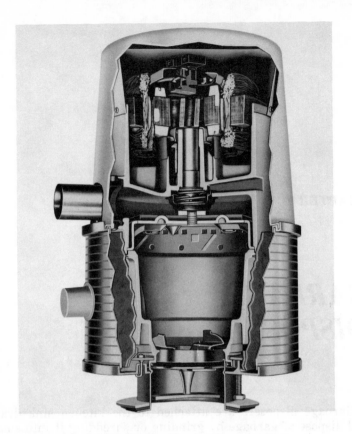

Fig. 7-1. Cutaway view of interior of garbage disposer.

The flow of water and the slope of the evacuation chamber cause the particles to enter the drain and flow out to the main stack of the drain system.

ELECTRICAL SYSTEM

Garbage disposers generally operate on 115-volt, single-phase, alternating current. While the motor current is rated at about 4 or 5 amperes, the varying load conditions to which the appliance is subjected require a 15- or 20-ampere fuse. Also, because the load may vary, particularly at start, a thermal-delay fuse is recommended. This makes it necessary to install a separate branch line to the disposer.

Garbage disposer motors are usually ⅓ to ½ HP. They may be capacitor start, induction run, or split-phase motors, of approximately 1700 r.p.m.

Garbage disposers are started either by a separate switch on a nearby wall, or by a switch actuated by the screwing on of the cover. In the latter case, an interlock on the cover prevents the operation of the disposer unless the cover is securely seated.

Fig. 7-2 shows two wiring diagrams typical of garbage disposers.

Since jamming is commonplace in the functioning of a garbage disposer, most disposers provide either an automatic or manual reversing switch, which by reversing the direction of the motor, frees the jammed material so that normal operation may resume.

Fig. 7-3 shows an automatic reversing switch that is operated by the unit cover, which depresses a plunger when placed in the operating position. The switch is a single-pole, single-throw, normally off, momentarily on switch. If the disposer jams or stalls, it will pause for a brief period in the jammed position, then will automatically reverse its direction. To change the direction back to its original one, it is necessary to stop and start the machine by turning the cover. In the reverse direction, the shredding action is not nearly as fast or efficient. The user should be instructed to change back to the original direction whenever jamming and reversing occurs. One well known make provides an off-on switch that continues to reverse the motor's polarity until the threat of a jam has been removed. In this particular make disposer, the grinding action is equally efficient in either motor direction.

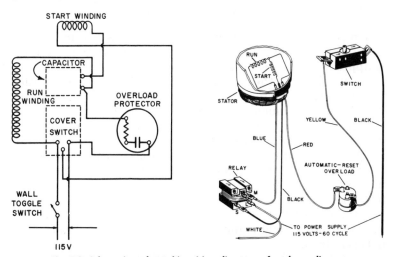

Fig. 7-2. Schematic and graphic wiring diagrams of garbage disposers.

Other disposers provide a reversing toggle switch with three positions: On, Off, and a spring-loaded momentary reverse which must be held down manually.

In addition to the reversing switches, most disposer motors

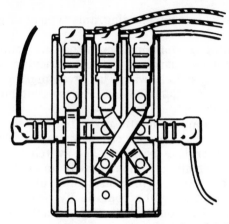

Fig. 7-3. Automatic reversing switch is used to clear jams.

are equipped with a thermal overload protector, which will either reset automatically when the overload condition subsides, or be reset manually by the user. The overload button is normally located under the unit and is reached by the user through a door in the sink apron.

INSTALLATION

A moderate flow of water (2 to 3 gallons per minute) is required for efficient operation of the disposer. Disposers are equipped with flanges to permit them to adapt to most normal drain openings in the bottom of the sink. Neoprene or other flexible mounting rings not only provide a watertight joint, but also absorb much of the disposer vibration.

A separate drain line (Fig. 7-4) to the main drain stack should be provided. This line should have its own trap, equipped with sanitary fittings (no internal edges or projections to catch and hold particles). Drain line diameter is normally prescribed by local plumbing codes—usually a minimum of 1½ inch pipe.

If the installation is to be in a second tub of the sink, the regular drain should empty into the main stack ahead of the disposer drain.

Drain lines should slope down a minimum pitch of 1 inch

for each running foot of pipe. Many plumbing codes require that a drain line be 2-inch pipe if the run exceeds 6 feet.

Disposers may be used in homes served by a septic tank of 750 to 1000 gallons capacity, depending on the number of persons served. If the septic tank has a grease trap, the disposer drain line must by-pass the trap. Most building and plumbing codes forbid the use of a disposer in homes equipped with a cesspool.

However, even in homes served by sewers, it may be necessary to obtain municipal permission to install a disposer. Permission sometimes takes the form of a tax.

Most disposers provide an inlet for connecting the drain from a dishwasher. The inlet fitting is generally of the swivel type for easy installation.

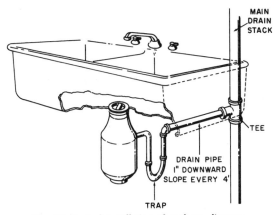

Fig. 7-4. Typical installation of garbage disposer.

TROUBLESHOOTING GUIDE

Users should be instructed in the proper use of the disposer to prevent minor failures and nuisance calls. Some users do not understand the need for cold water, believing that hot water will do the job more efficiently. Actually, hot water may slow the action. Cold water is used because it solidifies grease, which may then be ground up and washed away.

Daily flushing is recommended by most manufacturers. Fill the sink with three or four inches of cold water and remove the unit cover so the water will drain as rapidly as possible. An occasional flushing with baking soda is also beneficial. Mix the soda in a container with very hot water. Turn the unit on and let the detergent solution run through the machine. Flush immediately with cold water as described above.

173

Generally speaking, all organic matter with the exception of clam and oyster shells can be disposed of without difficulty. Large bones, string, excessive amounts of paper toweling, metal, glass, or other inorganic materials should not be placed in the disposer.

Following are some of the more frequent symptoms of failure and their causes and remedies.

Abnormal Noise and Vibration

1. A piece of inorganic matter may be loose in the grinding chamber, being knocked about by the impeller vane. Remove.
2. Impeller vane broken. Replace impeller.
3. Look for motor bearing damage and repair or replace as necessary.
4. In some instances, mounting flanges and drain connections may be loose. Tighten.

Slow Disposing

1. May be caused by string or other unacceptable matter. Clean out.
2. Impellers and shredders sometimes become worn with continued use, dulling the cutting edges. They cannot be sharpened—replacement of these components is indicated.
3. Insufficient water flow.

Slow Drain

1. Shredder teeth may be clogged. Clean with baking soda solution. Advise customers to always drain dishwater from the sink, then turn on cold water with disposer motor running to remove all traces of detergent.
2. Clogged drain. Check drain lines, trap. This cause would result in the same symptom even when the disposer is not operating.

Erratic Operation—Won't Start

1. Check all switches, motor, overload, wiring harness for continuity (see Chapter 1). Make sure user understands use of manually re-set overload protector.

Won't Stop

1. Defective switch, short in wiring, or wires crossed. Check against wiring diagrams.

CHAPTER 8

ROOM AIR CONDITIONERS

For a better understanding of the theory of cooling, review Chapter 2, Refrigerators and Freezers. The general principles of cooling outlined in Chapter 2 apply equally as well to the functioning of a room air conditioner. Hence, to get a general idea of how an air conditioner works, visualize the interior of a room as being the same as the interior of a refrigerator or freezer.

A block diagram (Fig. 8-1) of an air-conditioner system would be virtually the same as one for a refrigerator. Some minor differences would be reflected in the air flow pattern of an air conditioner, as compared to the gravity-flow pattern of air in the refrigerator. The main consideration in a good air-conditioning system is to force air circulation in every corner of the room, no easy task when rooms are long and narrow, or oddly shaped.

A room air conditioner circulates air in a room by means of a blower wheel operated by a separate blower motor. Having expelled air out of the front of the air conditioner cabinet, replacement air is drawn in through air inlets usually found at the bottom or sides of the cabinet. This air (sometimes mixed with some outside air) is then led across the evaporator, where it gives up some of its heat to the energy-starved re-

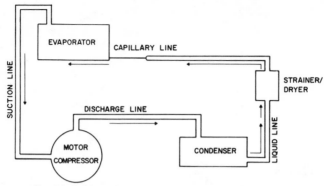

Fig. 8-1. Refrigeration system in a typical room air conditioner

frigerant vapor circulating inside the evaporator coils. Having been cooled, the air now gives up its moisture in the form of condensate which is led outdoors or blown across the coils of the condenser.

The air is now returned to the room, approximately 10 degrees cooler and considerably drier than it was when it entered the air conditioner.

The refrigerant, having absorbed some of the heat from the passing room air, is circulated by the compressor into a condenser under high pressure. The condenser is situated outside the conditioned room, where it draws outside air over its coils to absorb heat from the compressed refrigerant.

The continual cycling of the room air, giving up a little of its heat and moisture each time, gradually causes the room to dispel its heat outdoors and reduce the interior temperature to a comfortable level.

The same principles of sensible verses latent heat, the heat-absorbing properties of the process of vaporization, and the cycling of a refrigerant from a liquid to a vapor apply to an air conditioner as well as to a refrigerator or freezer.

ELECTRICAL SYSTEM

In a typical wiring diagram (Fig. 8-2) of a room air conditioner, the circuit can be traced from the three-wire power cord through the system. The switch is mechanically designed so that the fan motor may be operated either alone or with the compressor, but the compressor may never be operated unless the fan motor is on.

In a normal operating sequence, current is applied to the motor compressor through the overload protector, which opens the compressor circuit in the event of excessive line voltage or current drain should the compressor become stuck. Initially, the start capacitor is in the circuit until normal run speed is achieved, at which time it is disconnected by the relay. The run capacitor and both the start and run windings (S and R on the compressor terminals) remain in the circuit during compressor operation.

The thermostat disconnects the motor compressor on reaching a preselected low-temperature reading of inlet air. The fan motor, however, is not governed by the thermostat, but

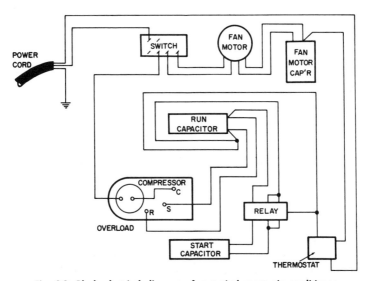

Fig. 8-2. Block electrical diagram of a typical room air conditioner.

continues to operate as long as the selector switch is in the On position. There are usually two speed settings for the fan—Normal Fan and High. These two speeds are accomplished with two sets of motor windings.

Thermostat

The thermostat determines the cycling periods of the compressor. As Fig. 8-3 shows, it consists of a short length of tubing sealed at one end, and filled with refrigerant. At the other end of the tubing is a bellows connected to a triggering device. A spring counteracts the expansion of the bellows.

With the bulk of the tubing in the return air stream, changes in temperature will cause the refrigerant, and, in turn, the bellows, to expand and contract. As the room becomes warmer, the expanding refrigerant tends to straighten the bellows against the force of the spring. When the bellows has expanded sufficiently, a lever closes the switch mechanism, completing the circuit. Electric current is now permitted to reach the compressor motor, which drives the compressor.

As the air in the room becomes cooler, so does the return air to the conditioner. At this point, the refrigerant in the thermostat tubing contracts. The bellows, under pressure of the counteracting spring, also contracts and a lever triggers the switch to open the contacts.

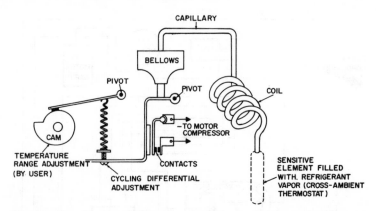

Fig. 8-3. Operation of a bellows-type thermostat employed in air conditioners.

A cross-ambient type thermostat employs a sensing tube or bulb at the end of a capillary line, permitting the bulb to be placed in the air stream and the body of the thermostat in any other convenient location on the instrument panel.

A knob on the thermostat controls the temperature at which the thermostat will cycle the compressor on and off. This knob is usually coupled with the counteracting spring in the bellows to increase or decrease the spring pressure. A dial indicates the direction in which to turn the knob for cooler or warmer operation. Numbers are sometimes used, but only as reference points; they have no significance regarding the temperature.

To prevent too frequent cycling of the compressor, the manufacturer sets a high and low limit in the thermostat. At the high limit, the thermostat contacts will close, and at the low limit they will open. The *differential*, as it is called, between high and low is usually about 5°F. The differential, as we have seen in the electric range section, is set by the manufacturer and may not be changed. Adjustments may be made, however, to the *range* of a thermostat to cause it to cycle at lower or higher temperatures.

If the thermostat were wired directly to an electric current, without a switch to open and close the contacts, their points would edge toward each other so slowly as the temperature rose that the current would jump across the open space between them before they could close positively. This is called arcing, and if permitted to continue, soon burns out the contacts. To prevent arcing, the contacts should open and close with a snap. This is usually accomplished by a toggle switch (Fig. 8-4). When the fork in the drawing moves up to the

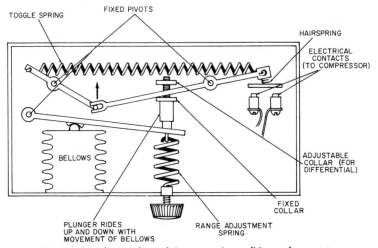

Fig. 8-4. Toggle switch used in many air conditioner thermostats.

level of the pivots, the least additional travel upward will cause the toggle spring to push the fork all the way up quickly, closing the electrical circuit. The opposite action occurs when the bellows contracts. Mercury switches and magnetic switches may also be employed for the same function.

Power Supply and Capacity

Air conditioners may operate either on 115-volt or 230-volt alternating current. Restrictions on the types of controls used, fan motors, and other components require power supplies of three-wire, single-phase, 60-cycle current. The wiring diagram shown in Fig. 8-5 is typical of most room air conditioners.

Air conditioners are rated as to capacity in Btu per hour. 12,000 Btu is the equivalent of a "ton of refrigeration." This is also a rate of cooling, or, more exactly, the amount of heat a specified amount of ice absorbs in a 24-hour period. Thus, a half-ton (6,000 Btu) air conditioner theoretically removes from a space the same amount of heat absorbed by 1,000 pounds of ice that had melted completely in a 24-hour period. Most air-conditioner serial plates express capacity in Btu per hour.

Horsepower is another rating of an air conditioner, but it properly refers to the power source, rather than the capacity. At best it can give only a rough indication of the capacity of

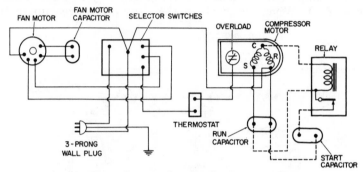

Fig. 8-5. Wiring diagram of a typical room air conditioner.

the entire system. The rest depends on such factors as the compressor cylinder displacement, rate of flow of the refrigerant, cubic feet per minute of air flow, and the capacities of the evaporator and condenser. Unlike the relationship between tons of refrigeration and Btu per hour, no clearcut relationship exists between horsepower and cooling capacity.

Since the larger horsepower motors driving the motor compressor require more power to perform their work efficiently, units having motors of greater than ¾ horsepower must be wired to a 230-volt power source.

MECHANICAL COMPONENTS

The mechanical components of an air conditioner perform in almost the same fashion as those of a refrigerator—indeed, many of these components bear the same name.

Compressor

In all important respects, the compressor (Fig. 8-6) of an air conditioner is the same as the compressor of a refrigerator. The electric motor driving the compressor pump is sealed in the same housing, preventing the loss of refrigerant and the absorption of outside air. Compressors are usually internally mounted.

Evaporator Blower

In most air conditioners, the evaporator blower takes the form of a "squirrel cage," (a shortened drum with fins parallel to its axis) (Fig. 8-7). This design is preferred because it is relatively quiet in operation, but nevertheless, it delivers an adequate volume of air.

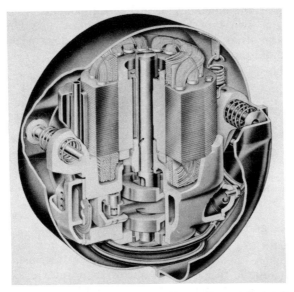

(Courtesy Tecumseh Products Co.)

Fig. 8-6. Internally mounted hermetically sealed "pancake" motor compressor.

The blower, located just behind the evaporator fins, blows return room air (or fresh outside air, depending on the setting of the selector switch) across the evaporator and into the room.

Condenser Fan

A ring-mounted fan just behind the condenser blows outside air across the condenser and back outdoors again. In some air conditioners, the condenser fan also picks up the condensate formed when the room air passed over the cold evaporator and blows it across the condenser fins to further hasten the cooling of the refrigerant in the condenser.

Both the evaporator blower and the condenser fan are driven by the same motor.

Filter

Placed in the return air stream, the filter (Fig. 8-8) traps and holds dust particles, as well as smoke, pollen, and other foreign matter.

The filter not only cleanses the air in the room, but also prevents dirt and lint from reaching the interior of the air conditioner. Dust on an evaporator or condenser may seriously impair the efficiency of either component.

There are two types of filters in general use. One is disposable; the other, a permanent type, may be washed, following the manufacturer's directions.

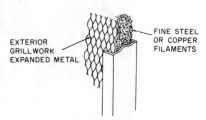

EXTERIOR GRILLWORK EXPANDED METAL

FINE STEEL OR COPPER FILAMENTS

Fig. 8-7. Construction of a squirrel-cage blower wheel.

Fig. 8-8. Filter construction.

Air Ducts and Plenum

Air ducts are used with some multiroom air conditioners and in central conditioning systems. They are usually quite heavily insulated to keep heat out of their interiors.

A plenum is any space within an air conditioner where air must travel (for instance, the space between the blower and evaporator).

HEAT-PUMP AIR CONDITIONERS

Heat pump is the name given to a room air conditioner that also works as an auxiliary heater for between-seasons heating, or as the prime source of heat in winter. Simply stated, a heat pump works by reversing the flow of refrigerant, to warm a conditioned space instead of cooling it.

If the construction of an evaporator facilitates extracting heat from the surrounding air, it also permits conduction of heat to the surrounding air. Similarly, the heat transfer ability of a condenser works as well absorbing heat as dispelling it.

Think about the ocean for a moment; even on the coldest winter day, the temperature of the ocean in temperate climates rarely falls much below 40°F. This means that, although it is too cold for animal survival, the ocean still has an enormous amount of heat stored up in its depths. The same thing is true, to a lesser degree, about the air surrounding us. Although the temperature may fall to −50°F, there is still *some* heat in the cold air.

A heat pump extracts some of this heat from the outside air. In order to do this, the refrigerant in the system, normally used to extract heat from indoor air, is circulated in the opposite direction by means of a reverse-cycle valve. Refrigerant vapor flows from the compressor to the evaporator (indoor coil) under compression. Blowers pass room air over the indoor coil, causing the refrigerant to give up its heat and condense to a liquid. The liquid refrigerant passes through the restrictor tubing (or expansion valve) into the condenser (outdoor coil). Here it absorbs heat from the surrounding outdoor air, boils into vapor and passes into the compressor again.

Remember that heat flows from substances of higher temperature to substances of lower temperature. In order for the heat pump to work properly, the refrigerant must have a vaporizing temperature, or boiling point, lower than the temperature of the surrounding air, even if only a few degrees lower. While this would appear to limit the performance of a heat pump, recent improvements in refrigerants and mechanical pumping have made the heat pump a very efficient mechanism. Some models generate so much heat that the front panel and deflector grilles must be fabricated from a special plastic that does not warp or blister.

Figs. 8-9 and 8-10 show the difference between the cooling phase and the heating phase of a heat-pump air conditioner. Note that an electrically stimulated solenoid activates the reverse-cycle valve. The electrical impulse for the solenoid is supplied by the room thermostat, which automatically reverses the refrigerant flow whenever the room temperature drops to a predetermined low. In earlier models of the heat-pump air conditioner, the refrigerant flow was reversed by a hand valve.

As with any evaporator, cooling of the surrounding air is accompanied by condensation. During the reverse operation, this condensate may freeze when the temperature of the outdoor coil drops below 32°F and the outside temperature drops below 45°F (with variations due to the amount of moisture

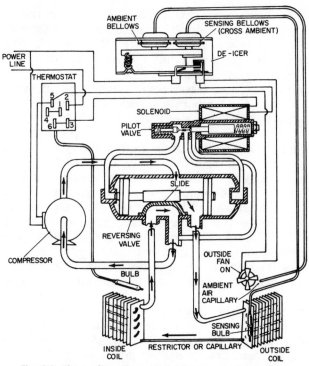

Fig. 8-9. The cooling phase of the heat-pump air conditioner.

in the air, construction of the heat pump, and other factors).
The outside coils become blanketed with ice, reducing the heat
transfer efficiency of the coils.

A de-icer is introduced into the system to overcome the
effects of ice (Fig. 8-11). It consists of a pair of bellows containing refrigerant. One bellows is connected to a sensing tube
on the outside coil. The other is connected to an ambient sensing tube, which senses only the temperature of the air surrounding the coil.

As the ice blanket increases in thickness, less heat is transferred between the air and coil, causing the temperature of the
coil to drop. When the temperature difference between air and
coil becomes great enough, the de-icer (1) opens the circuit
to the outside coil fan, and (2) sends an electrical impulse to
the thermostat, causing the solenoid to operate the reverse-
cycle valve. Refrigerant then flows in the normal cooling cycle,
which means the condenser (outside coil) will become warm
enough to melt the ice. As the temperature difference between
the air and coil lessens, the de-icer circuit opens, the thermo-

stat regains control, and the reverse cycle valve once more reverses the flow of refrigerant to the heating cycle. At the same time, the outside coil fan resumes operation, and the heat pump continues the heating cycle until an accumulation of ice again initiates the de-icing sequence.

INSTALLATION

Two things should be uppermost in mind when installing an air conditioner. The first is the safety of the installation, from both a physical and electrical standpoint. The second is the efficiency of the unit, which will be greatly affected by the type of installation.

A proper installation will not *improve* the efficiency of the unit, but it will permit the unit to work at its rated capacity. On the other hand, an improper installation may seriously impair the cooling efficiency, and may even lay the groundwork for premature failure.

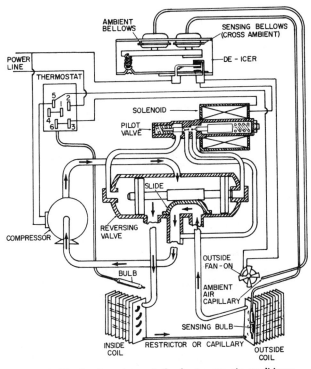

Fig. 8-10. The heating phase of the heat-pump air conditioner.

The most common installation for a room air conditioner is through the window, mounted on the window sill. Other mounting methods are *transom,* and *through-the-wall* installations. Certain console models are available which are mounted beneath a window, with ductwork leading through the window above it for discharging and admitting outside air to cool the condenser.

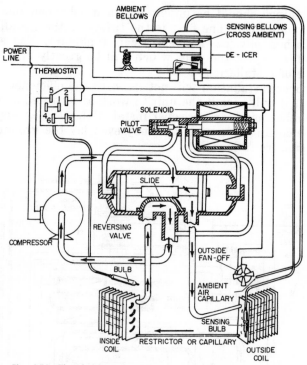

Fig. 8-11. The de-icing phase of the heat-pump air conditioner.

A window installation is the easiest of all these types. Transom installations are sometimes necessary in stores and offices having only large plate-glass windows. A through-the-wall installation is not usually warranted because of the expense involved in reconstruction, repainting and/or repapering. However, where there are no windows in the wall that is the only logical location for the unit, a through-the-wall installation may still be the best alternative.

Manufacturers of room air conditioners supply installation kits, which are designed to meet almost any requirement. It is necessary to know the kind of installation (double-hung

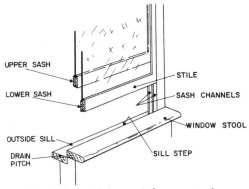

Fig. 8-12. Double-hung window construction.

window, casement, etc.) when ordering the air conditioner, so that the proper kit may be supplied with the unit. Instructions for installation are provided with the kits.

Window Installation

Fig. 8-12 shows a typical double-hung window and Fig. 8-13 a typical casement window. The latter is usually made of metal framing, opening to the outside on side hinges. Note the nomenclature of the various parts of the windows—it will be helpful in following the steps of the installation procedure.

Double-Hung Window—In a double-hung window installation, the air conditioner is anchored firmly on the sill, prevented from tipping over by side frames which slide out from the unit cabinet and engage side angle brackets fitted into

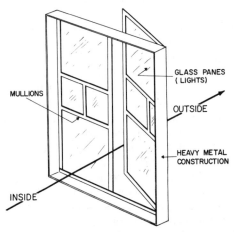

Fig. 8-13. Casement window construction.

the sash channels (Fig. 8-14). Further support is obtained by attaching the top bracket to the sash stile. In some installations, it is necessary to attach the air conditioner to the stool as well as to the outside sill by means of channels. Because the height and pitch of sill steps may vary, manufacturers provide a means for adjusting the pitch of the cabinet (about ¼ inch per foot) so that it tilts to the outside, allowing condensate to fall directly to the ground rather than run down the walls.

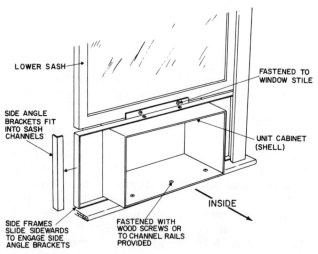

LOWER SASH

FASTENED TO
WINDOW STILE

SIDE ANGLE
BRACKETS FIT
INTO SASH
CHANNELS

UNIT CABINET
(SHELL)

INSIDE

SIDE FRAMES
SLIDE SIDEWARDS
TO ENGAGE SIDE
ANGLE BRACKETS

FASTENED WITH
WOOD SCREWS OR
TO CHANNEL RAILS
PROVIDED

Fig. 8-14. Simplified diagram of a typical double-hung
window installation.

The height and width of the clear space with the sash open must, of course, be great enough to admit the air conditioner cabinet. Normally, the height of the air conditioner will be no problem, since most double-hung windows are high enough.

To fill the space created by varying widths of windows, all installation kits are provided with side filler panels, usually made of composition board, to fit any space (up to 40 inches) not taken up by the width of the cabinet. For wider windows, special installation kits are provided. To adapt the filler panel to the space to be filled, only one vertical cut is necessary. Some side panels have grooves spaced about ½ inch apart; the panel can be broken cleanly at the desired groove by placing it over a sharp edge, as shown in Fig. 8-15.

Now look at the typical installation diagram in Fig. 8-16. It is desirable to get the room air conditioner as high off the

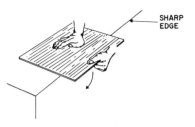

Fig. 8-15. Breaking a side panel along the grooved lines.

floor as possible, because cold air sinks. However, because the unit requires a firm base, it is normally installed in the lower sash opening of a double-hung window, where it can rest on the sill.

For a neat installation, the unit should be centered in the window, with side panels of equal width on either side. First mark off the center of the sill; this mark will serve as the basis for all measurements. The instructions contained in the

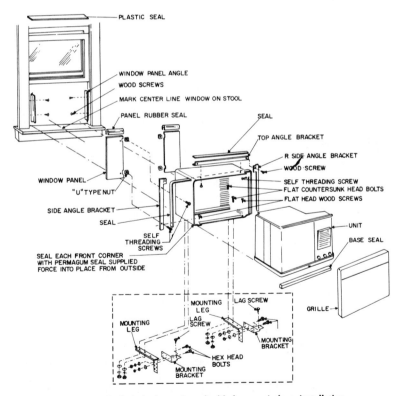

Fig. 8-16. Exploded view of a double-hung window installation.

kit will usually give measurements, with allowances already figured in for unit width, height and other known dimensions.

In the installation shown, the side angle brackets are first screwed into the recesses of the sash channels on each side of the window frame. Now the cabinet is slid off the unit. The center line of the cabinet is lined up with the center line marked off on the sill, and the cabinet is positioned for (1) inside flush mounting, (2) outside flush mounting, or (3) middle mounting (Fig. 8-17). Most cabinets are provided with knockout holes for alternate mountings, and button plugs to seal the unused holes.

After the air conditioner has been correctly positioned, frames are extended to engage the side angle brackets. This, will hold the cabinet securely in position. The seal strip is

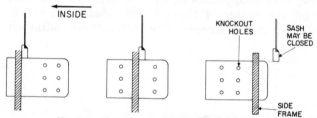

Fig. 8-17. Three types of window mountings.

positioned on the top of the cabinet, and the sash lowered. Now pilot holes are drilled into the sill and window stile; they should be smaller than the screws but not so small that the wood will crack when the screws are installed. The sash is raised again, and the side panels inserted, cut to fit into the space between the side of the cabinet and the window channel.

Some installation kits provide a means for wedging the side panels tightly. A wedging member with diagonally slotted screw holes is supplied which, when pushed downward, closes tightly against the panels. Foam, neoprene or rubber seals may also be supplied; these fit over the top edge of the side panels, making a tight seal between the panels and bottom of the sash.

The cabinet is then screwed down securely into the window stool (or into front and rear channels if provided), the sash is lowered and the top bracket is screwed to the window stile. Usually, it is desirable to also lock the upper sash in the closed position by fitting blocks of wood into the sash channels. Any small gaps at joints and corners should be plugged with plastic foam or other insulation. This material, usually supplied with the kit, should be packed into the gaps from the outside.

The unit should then be slid into the cabinet (usually on the tracks provided on the cabinet floor) and secured with the bolts and nuts provided. Some air conditioners have externally mounted compressors—that is, their spring mounts are on the outside of the housing. These compressors are usually tied down for shipping by brackets or clamps which must be removed before the compressor is started. Externally mounted compressors also have provisions for leveling, which should also be attended to before running the unit. The final step, after replacing the front panel, is to plug in the unit.

Some local building codes may limit the distance a unit may extend beyond the building line, therefore, be sure to check local ordinances and codes before planning an installation. In any event, if the unit extends more than a foot beyond the outer sill, it would be wise to use wall brackets (available with most installation kits) for further support.

Casement Window Installation—Casement windows pose special problems for the installer. Fig. 8-18 shows a specially constructed room air conditioner which fits *standard* casement window openings of 16⅛-inch width and any height greater than about 30 inches. The entire casement window and all its hardware are removed and the air conditioner is placed in the frame opening. (A filler panel covers any excess space above the unit.) It is only necessary to secure the unit to the metal framing, being sure to weatherstrip all junctures. Proper pitch for these units is automatic—that is, if the unit is properly mounted, the condensate will drip toward the outside of the building.

The unit just described is mounted wholly outside the room, with the front facing into the room. Because the unit is mounted to a metal frame, it needs no elaborate bracing, even though it may extend beyond the building line.

In the foregoing installation, the unit is designed to fit into a standard space exactly. Casement windows that are too wide for this type of installation entail much more work. It is necessary to cut the glass panes to the dimensions of the back of the cabinet (Fig. 8-19). This may mean cutting part of single panes. (Sometimes a neater installation may be had by replacing the glass panes with composition board. The window mullions are *not* cut—all that is required is free passage of air to and from the condenser.)

The air conditioner is then mounted flush with the casement window (while closed). A foam-rubber gasket seals the juncture between the edges of the cut glass panes (or composition board) and the back of the cabinet. A two-pass condenser air

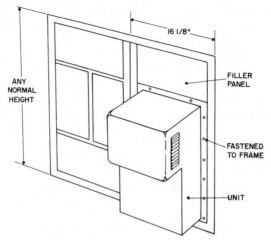

Fig. 8-18. Room air conditioner specifically constructed to fit a standard casement window.

conditioner is necessary for this installation. This type of unit is open only in the back—it has no side louvers.

Transom installations—Fig. 8-20 shows the salient features of this type of installation. Since the air conditioner is mounted above a door, consideration must be given to the people who pass beneath it, both from the point of view of safety and with regard to the drip of condensate. Heavy duty straps, securely anchored in place, support the air conditioner from the ceiling, rather than permitting it to rest on the less secure door-

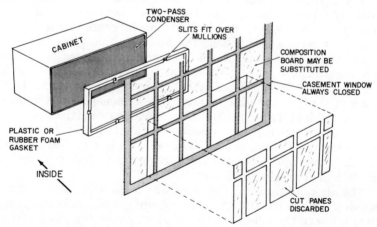

Fig. 8-19. Cutting the glass panes for a wide casement window installation.

way framing. Condensate, of course, must be piped to the outdoors or into a drain.

If the doorway under the transom opens into a passageway or short hall, air flow may present a problem. Also, doors are frequently recessed back from the building line and the outside air must then be drawn in from beneath an overhanging eave or balcony. As a result, outside air may recirculate through the condenser, greatly impairing efficiency.

Another problem, where the air conditioner is located next to a short hall, is recirculation of *cooled* air in which newly cooled air re-enters the air intakes of the air conditioner immediately after it emerges from the evaporator blower. This may cause a freeze inside the unit—it will certainly result in very poor performance.

Both these conditions may be partially corrected by installing suitable ductwork leading to open areas, although it is far better to avoid the situation entirely by finding an alternate location.

Through-the-wall installation—Fig. 8-21 shows the framing necessary to prepare for a through-the-wall installation.

Walls, because they have greater area than windows, offer a much more flexible choice for the location of a unit. This can be a great help when planning air conditioning for long, narrow rooms or rooms with odd shapes. A through-the-wall installation can be reinforced with heavy framing, making it unnecessary to support the overhang with unsightly brackets. Also, it is possible to mount the unit so that the front will be perfectly flush with the inside wall. Also, weatherstripping

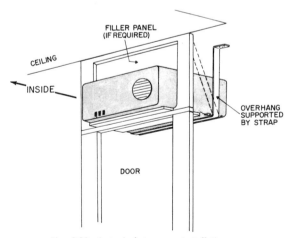

Fig. 8-20. A typical transom installation.

a wall opening is likely to be far more effective than attempting to caulk all the many avenues of heat entry around a double-hung window.

The opening in the wall must be made large enough to permit fitting the rough framing and molding around the cabinet. Be doubly sure that the unit has the proper pitch, and all louvers and air-return openings are unobstructed. Finish framing may be supplied with the unit, or millwork may have to be installed on both the inside and outside walls for an attractive installation.

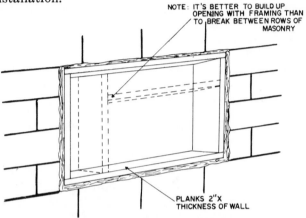

NOTE: IT'S BETTER TO BUILD UP OPENING WITH FRAMING THAN TO BREAK BETWEEN ROWS OF MASONRY

PLANKS 2"X THICKNESS OF WALL

Fig. 8-21. Framing an opening through masonry for a through-the-wall installation.

INSTALLATION CHECK LIST

1. Make sure the *unit* has the correct pitch for proper drainage. This pitch (¼ inch per foot) may be "built-in" or the cabinet may have to be pitched (consult the installation kit instructions).
2. If storm windows are installed in the window, the sill may have to be built up so that the cabinet will clear the bottom rail of the storm-window frame.
3. If return air is admitted to the unit through openings in the bottom front of the cabinet, make sure the window stool does not obstruct them. If necessary, build up the stool with lumber, allowing at least 1 inch between it and the cabinet.
4. If an outside flush mounting is planned, some means of carrying off the condensate should be provided to prevent unsightly streaking of outside walls. Drip pans are available in most installation kits.

5. If the installation results in an enclosed space where rain water may collect, drill drainage holes in the outside sill.
6. Since the outside air must be considerably cooler than the condenser temperature at all times, the air conditioner must be located in a wall with the least exposure to the direct rays of the afternoon sun. If necessary, provide an awning to shield the condenser from the sun, but be sure that nothing obstructs the free passage of air to and from the condenser.
7. Check the manufacturer's instructions carefully to make sure that they have been fully carried out. Be especially careful that all shipping brackets are removed.

REPAIRS

Understanding the theory and operation of an air conditioner is vital to good servicing. A thorough job of servicing, particularly the operations of adding refrigerant and evacuating the system, require great care, deliberate planning, and constant practice.

Refrigerant used in modern air conditioners is, in itself, harmless. However, it is delivered and stored in containers under fairly high pressure, and care is required in its handling. Never expose a cylinder of refrigerant to a temperature greater than 125°F. Do not allow refrigerant supply drums and cylinders to remain in the direct rays of the sun in hot weather. Adapters are available which attach to supply cylinders, affording a hand grip as well as protection for the cylinder valve.

Refrigerant Supply Containers

Refrigerant is supplied in large cylinders (Fig. 8-22) holding anywhere from 5 to 150 pounds of various types of refrigerant. Refrigerant may be taken directly from these supply cylinders, or may first be transferred to smaller-capacity service cylinders. Refrigerant for small charges is also supplied in cans holding from a few ounces to two or three pounds. Unlike the supply and service cylinders, these cans are disposable. An adapter at the top of the can accepts a universal valve for opening the can and dispensing the contents.

Evacuating A System

When adding a new charge to a system, the system must first be flushed, evacuated, and dehydrated—especially after any repairs or replacements have been made. Every speck of foreign matter and every microdroplet of moisture must be removed from the lines, compressor, and other components in the system.

Systems that have been opened must first be flushed out thoroughly; ordinarily this is done with the compressor and capillary restrictor removed or disconnected from the line. After flushing is completed and before evacuation takes place, the compressor is replaced in the line. New or reconditioned compressors are delivered with sealed suction and discharge lines, the compressor itself being charged with some refrigerant to keep out moisture while in transit or storage.

The flushing unit shown schematically in Fig. 8-23 may be used in flushing the system. The chart accompanying the illus-

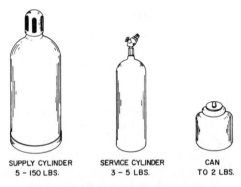

SUPPLY CYLINDER   SERVICE CYLINDER   CAN
5 – 150 LBS.   3 – 5 LBS.   TO 2 LBS.

Fig. 8-22. Types of refrigerant containers.

tration gives the positions of valves during charging, flushing, and evacuating. (Charging and evacuation, in this case, refer to the cleaning agent, not to the final evacuation and charging with the permanent charge of refrigerant.)

R-11 (trichloromonofluoromethane) is used as the cleaning agent because it remains in a liquid state at or near atmospheric pressure and normal room temperature. The liquid refrigerant circulates through the system, washing out any solder or dirt particles, oil, residue, bits of varnish from motor windings and other foreign matter, into a filter in the flushing unit. A sight glass in the pump line permits visual observation of the cleaning agent. When it shows clear in the glass, allow 10 or 15 minutes more circulation to make sure every particle of foreign matter is removed.

Capillary restrictors, which are disconnected from the line during flushing, should be replaced before charging the system. Exact replacements are required because of the critical nature of this component. If replacement is impossible, the tubing should be subjected to high-pressure cleaning to insure that the tiny opening (about .050 inch) is completely free.

Evacuating the system begins after it is thoroughly flushed out. A specially designed high vacuum pump (not to be confused with the liquid pump of the flushing unit) is required for the degree of vacuum necessary. Sealed systems require the use of tees in both the suction and discharge lines.

Charging the system may be accomplished by using the system compressor as described in Chapter 2, or by using a charging station in shop situations.

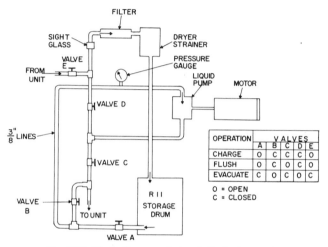

OPERATION	VALVES				
	A	B	C	D	E
CHARGE	O	C	C	C	O
FLUSH	O	C	O	C	O
EVACUATE	C	O	C	O	C

O = OPEN
C = CLOSED

Fig. 8-23. Block diagram of shop-built flushing unit using a liquid pump.

ELECTRICAL TESTS

The performance of a refrigerant under given conditions is predictable and unvarying. As a result, it is possible to gain information about the mechanical functioning of an air conditioner from electrical data, sometimes combining this data with pressure and temperature information. The following are some electrical tests that help in diagnosing the cause of air conditioner failures.

Temperature Split/Wattage Test

Information about air flow, compressor functioning, amount of charge, and other suspected troubles can be confirmed by temperature readings taken at the return room air inlet and the cooled air outlet, coupled with readings from a wattmeter.

This information is then compared to standards published by the manufacturer.

The difference in temperature between the inlet and outlet air flow is called a temperature split. High or low splits refer to a greater or less temperature difference, respectively. A low split, meaning a small difference between inlet and outlet temperatures, indicates insufficient cooling; and a high split, too much cooling.

Each of the following combinations of high and low splits and wattages has a special significance in servicing the air conditioner.

High temperature split, low wattage—An indication that an insufficient volume of air is passing over the evaporator. The lesser volume of air gives up more of its own heat to the evaporator, is delivered to the room at a colder temperature than normal. Look for obstructions in the air-flow system.

Low temperature split, low wattage—This indicates that the evaporator is starved for refrigerant. Look for restrictions in the capillary (or expansion valve, if there is one), air in the refrigerant lines, and mechanical faults. To find a restriction in a capillary tube or in any other tubing in the liquid line, feel the line for a cold spot, which indicates that a restriction exists just ahead of it. If no cold spots are present, the charge is low. Check for leaks in the system.

No temperature split, low wattage—This indicates a non-functioning compressor, due to a broken shaft, valves stuck open, etc.

High temperature split, high wattage—Usually this would indicate too much refrigerant in the system, a rare condition in sealed room air conditioners. Confirm by checking for sweating throughout the evaporator passes and the suction line. Too high a refrigerant charge will cause the compressor protector to open the circuit frequently; even permanently.

Low temperature split, high wattage—The high wattage indicates the compressor is working too hard. Look for sweating on the suction line all the way to the compressor, a sign that some liquid refrigerant is reaching the compressor. The system must be drained and the compressor, needle valves, and other components checked for damage. Look also for causes such as mechanical binding in the compressor.

Line Voltage

Low or high line voltage is a source of trouble in any air conditioner. When checking the line voltage, turn on any other appliance on the same branch line which ordinarily operates at the same time as the air conditioner. The air conditioner should be running at full load during the test. Also make sure that the wire sizes of any line cords are adequate.

Switches

With an ohmmeter, check for continuity across the terminals at each switch setting. *CAUTION—before making any tests with an ohmmeter, remove the power plug from the outlet.*

Overload Protector

Use a wattmeter and a jumper wire to check the overload protector on the motor compressor. Similarly, thermostats, start and run capacitors and relays are tested according to the instructions given in Chapter 1.

TROUBLESHOOTING GUIDE

The following symptoms are the signs of trouble in the system. Each symptom is followed by a number of possible causes and remedies. The list is by no means complete, but it will serve as a guide to the more common failures and causes of failure in any air-conditioning system.

Compressor and Fan Motor Do Not Run

1. No power to system. Check supply lines, outlets, fuses, switches, internal circuitry. If a fuse is blown, check for possible high voltage, or shorts in the line. Merely replacing a fuse does not eliminate the cause.
2. Loose or faulty connections or switches. Adjust or replace as necessary.

Fan Motor Runs, But Compressor Does Not Function

1. Defective compressor start capacitor. See capacitor test in Chapter 1.
2. Circuit to compressor open. Check circuit, switches, terminals, overloads, relays.
3. Low voltage may be a contributing cause. Install transformer (available from the manufacturer for this purpose).
4. Defective thermostat or circuit to thermostat. Check as described in Chapter 1.
5. Defective motor compressor. When all other tests fail to turn up faulty electrical components, the compressor may be at fault. Apply power directly to it through the test cord. If compressor fails to run, it must be replaced.

Do not attempt to start a "stuck" compressor by applying a momentary surge of high voltage, as is sometimes done. This is a temporary remedy which may damage the compressor.

When a motor compressor burns out, the system must be thoroughly flushed and evacuated as described previously. All traces of burned insulation and varnish, carbon and other foreign matter must be removed from the system, as well as certain harmful acids which form as a result of burnout. The condenser, evaporator, and segments of the lines should be flushed separately. Do not attempt to reuse the capillary tubing. After a thorough flushing, the system is reassembled; all tubing except the capillary is resoldered securely, with tees installed in the suction and discharge lines for recharging. Flushing is again performed (without the capillary in the line), to get out all bits of solder and other foreign matter that may have collected in the reassembly procedure. The capillary is then soldered in the line, and refrigerant added to the system to check for pressure leaks. Now proceed with normal evacuation and recharging.

Fan Runs, Compressor Starts, Then Stops

1. Overload protector is operating. Check for high wattage caused by high voltage, clogged condenser, or any restriction in the refrigerant lines. Check for shorts in compressor circuit or relay.

2. Condenser air flow blocked, or outside temperature on unit casing so high that it approximates temperature of refrigerant in the condenser. Free the air flow path, or provide an awning for shading the outdoor portion of the unit.

3. Internal trouble in compressor. Check for wattage consumption as given in service literature. If abnormally high and no other trouble can be found in circuit, replacement of compressor is indicated.

No Air Flow, Compressor Runs

1. This is a serious situation, regardless of the cause. The air conditioner should never be permitted to run without the fan. In fact, most air conditioners are so wired that it is impossible to run the compressor unless the fan motor is operating. Look for binding of the fan motor shaft or fan blades, defective fan motor, shorted fan motor relays or capacitors.

200

Noisy Operation

1. Check for misaligned fan blades, loose tubing connections, loose compressor mountings, defective fan motor bearings, or other obvious mechanical faults.
2. Sometimes, after a prolonged shutdown, refrigerant will be absorbed in the compressor lubricant. This will make a noise like bubbling liquid. It will disappear after the unit is in operation for a time.
3. If the noises appear to come from within the compressor, and they do not stop after the unit has been in operation for a short while, internal trouble is indicated, such as broken mounting springs, loose shaft bearings, or worn piston rings. Compressor should be replaced.
4. Noise can result from the vibration of tubing or from "harmonics." Run a hand over the refrigerant tubing, particularly where it makes a loop before reaching the compressor. At the place where the touch of the hand causes the noise to stop, tape or clamp the tubing to the nearest inert component such as a bracket or frame member.

Insufficient Cooling

1. Look first for dirty evaporator and condenser coils. Even a light coating of dust can interfere with heat transfer to or from these vital components. Remove all dust with a vacuum cleaner; then see why it is entering the interior of the cabinet. Caution the operator never to run the unit without the air filter in place, and also to replace or clean the filter at frequent intervals, according to the manufacturer's operating instructions.
2. Those units that use the condensate from the evaporator for extra cooling of the condenser should be examined for proper adjustment of the slinger ring on the condenser fan.
3. Low fan speed may be the cause of insufficient cooling. Check the voltage, electrical circuit, fan lubricant, and look for bent or broken fan blades.
4. Too much superheated vapor in the evaporator passes will cause insufficient cooling. Look for leaks in the refrigerant system. Units with expansion valves require adjustment of the valve, added refrigerant or both. In sealed units with capillary restrictor tubing, look for cold spots in the liquid line—they indicate an internal obstruction. Check pressure-temperature relationships

against standards in service literature. Check also for low refrigerant level, although in sealed systems this is a remote possibility in the absence of leak evidence.

5. Ice on evaporator coils. Coupled with insufficient cooling, this is evidence of a low volume of air passing over the evaporator. Check air passages, fan motor operation, and restrictions at return air inlet. *Very important:* check to see whether cooled air is passing directly from the air conditioner outlet grilles to the return air intake. This is a possibility if the air conditioner is located in a corner of a room where cooled air may be prevented from freely circulating. Adjusting the grilles to direct air toward the open space in the room will frequently correct this situation. In extreme cases, duct work must be provided to carry the cooled air away from the return air intake.

Ice on the evaporator, along with too much cooling, is evidence of a defective thermostat. Check and replace if necessary.

Sweating

1. As mentioned previously, sweating of the suction line may be an indication of excess refrigerant in the system. For systems with expansion valves (not normally found in room air conditioners), this is corrected by adjusting the valve to admit less refrigerant into the evaporator. This increases the length of travel of the superheat at the end of the evaporator passes. In sealed systems, sweating may be a normal condition, or it may be caused by impairment of the air flow, either in the condenser or evaporator. Rarely, if ever, will sweating be caused by too much refrigerant in a sealed system.

CHAPTER 9

HUMIDIFIERS AND
DEHUMIDIFIERS

Humidifiers add moisture to the air in home, office or factory; dehumidifiers remove excess moisture. The degree of humidity is linked closely with how comfortable we feel. It is almost as important a factor as the temperature of the air.

Outside winter air at a typical 20°F. and 40% relative humidity will drop to only 6% relative humidity when heated indoors to 72°F. This is drier than the driest desert. Air at 6% relative humidity will steal moisture from every kind of material it may come into contact with: wood, glue, paper, food, skin and the linings of mouth, nose and throat.

Air that has an adequate relative humidity helps preserve the joints in furniture, makes draperies last longer and makes us feel better. Moreover, it takes less heat to make us feel comfortable at 40% relative humidity than at 10% relative humidity—a saving in fuel. By the same token, high humidity in summer causes great discomfort. Lowering the relative humidity of summer air contributes to our well-being, allows us to bear higher temperatures than normally.

Generally speaking, a humidifier is used primarily in the winter to make air more comfortable by adding moisture. A dehumidifier is used primarily in summer to make air more comfortable by removing moisture. The latter appliance has wide use in commercial and industrial establishments, where an even moisture content is a requirement, such as in lithographic printing establishments. On the other hand, humidifiers are often used in textile industries even in summer, where a high moisture content lessens the chance of breaking threads.

A dehumidifier is nothing more than a miniature condenser/evaporator, much the same as the system found in a refrigerator or air conditioner. The important difference is that the heat energy of the air is not discharged to the outdoors, but is recirculated along with the air, which has had some of its moisture content removed. A drip pan or water discharge line carries off the water that is removed from the air.

A dehumidifier does not cool the air it treats. Actually, due to the heat of the compressor, it may even add a little heat to the ambient temperature. Another difference between the systems is that the suction line of the dehumidifier has a larger inside diameter, allowing a lower compression (about 40 pounds per square inch gauge above sea level atmospheric pressure, compared to 50 psig and higher encountered in refrigerators and air conditioners). This, in turn, permits lighter, less expensive compressors and other components. Servicing a dehumidifier, then, is similar to servicing any refrigerator or air conditioning system.

HUMIDIFIER OPERATION

Humidifiers work in several different ways. They may be free-standing units, operating independently to treat the air in several adjacent rooms, or they may be hooked into the air duct system of a warm air furnace. Some humidifiers simply sling a continuous belt through a pan of water, with a blower positioned at the top of the belt's travel to blow moisture laden air into a register.

Other humidifiers (Fig. 9-1) scoop up water from the surface of a water-filled pan, by means of centrifugal force fling it against the sides of a perforated cylinder and through a vaporizing "comb" that breaks up the water into a fine mist. This mist is directed into the room or into the main air duct of the warm air furnace to each room in the house. One popular make of humidifier permits water to trickle over a "cell" panel, consisting of a series of tiny holes. A blower fan directs a stream of air through the cell panel, creating the fine mist that is then injected into the furnace main supply air duct.

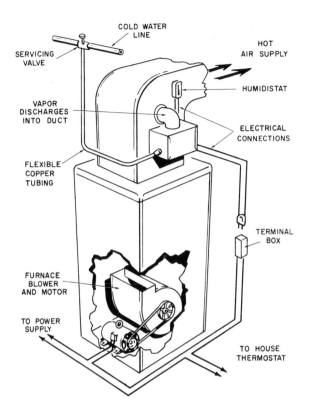

COLD WATER LINE

SERVICING VALVE

HOT AIR SUPPLY

HUMIDISTAT

VAPOR DISCHARGES INTO DUCT

ELECTRICAL CONNECTIONS

FLEXIBLE COPPER TUBING

TERMINAL BOX

FURNACE BLOWER AND MOTOR

TO POWER SUPPLY

TO HOUSE THERMOSTAT

Fig. 9-1. A typical home humidifier system.

Humidifiers mounted in warm air furnace plenums are generally connected in series with the furnace blower motor, so the humidifier works only when the blower is operating. In some installations, this is the only control, although a degree of control may be provided by regulating the amount of water flowing to the humidifier.

For positive control, most humidifiers employ a humidistat as shown in Fig. 9-2, a device which measures the amount of moisture in air. The humidistat is mounted in the main air duct, just before delivery to the branches of the system. When the moisture content of the air it is sampling drops below its bottom range, a pair of electrical contacts close. With the main furnace blower in operation, the humidifier will start up and continue to operate until the moisture content increases to a point above the upper limit of the humidistat's range, or when the blower stops, having been turned off by the satisfied temperature thermostat of the main house.

Humidistats also employ a setting which may be operated by the customer. Typical settings are shown in Table 9-1.

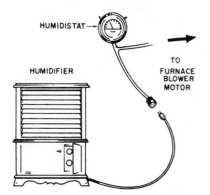

Fig. 9-2. A humidistat used to control the moisture in the air.

Table 9-1. Percentage of Relative Humidity

At Outside Temperature °F.	Recommended Setting
—20	15% Relative Humidity
—10	20% Relative Humidity
0	25% Relative Humidity
+10	30% Relative Humidity
+20	35% Relative Humidity
above 20	40% Relative Humidity

MAINTENANCE AND SERVICING

Community supplies of water contain a varying amount of solids held in suspension. These solids tend to accumulate in the reservoir, take-up and vaporizing systems. In time, the humidifier will require a thorough cleaning or it will become inefficient and inoperative. Most manufacturers recommend two cleanings during the heating season.

Cleaning is simply a matter of disassembling the working parts of the humidifier and scrubbing off the film of caked solids from component parts. Be sure that fins and teeth of vaporizing combs, perforated cylinders and evaporating cells are scrubbed clean and openings are clear. Moving parts, of course, should be lubricated where oil cups are provided.

Generally speaking, humidifiers are relatively trouble-free because they operate under constant conditions with a minimum of interference by the customer. They are sealed against dirt and leakage, eliminating the possibility of obstructions in the mechanical train.

To check the operation of the humidistat, follow these steps:

1. Turn humidistat to highest setting. If humidifier starts (provided furnace blower is operating) humidistat setting was satisfied by moisture content of air.
2. Using test lamp, check to see if power is available at humidistat.
3. Check to see if power is being supplied through the humidistat by turning the setting to the highest control. If no power, humidistat should be replaced.
4. Check for broken or loose wiring in motor component.
5. Repair or replace broken wiring or component containing the break—one that did not pass current to the test lamp.

CHAPTER 10

WATER
HEATERS

In its purest state, water is a compound of hydrogen and oxygen—as any schoolboy knows. However, even our clean, safe drinking water contains many impurities—suspended in solution. Some of these impurities are dissolved solids, such as chlorine, iron, magnesium, calcium, and other familiar metallic and organic substances.

Water mixes intimately with iron dissolved from earth and rocks, although probably as much iron is added to water from iron pipes as through natural sources. As the iron oxidizes, it turns water a rusty color. This iron rust is produced faster in hot water than in cold water. Whatever the source, high iron content in water is objectionable because it stains clothing, utensils, and plumbing fixtures.

As discussed in Chapter 3, the principle cause of "hardness" in water is the presence of calcium and magnesium—not iron. In addition to hardness, water has two other properties—it is either alkaline or acid.

Two factors tend to contribute to the corrosiveness of water —its *softness* and its *acidity*. Therefore, a balance must be struck between excessive softness and objectionable hardness, and between alkalinity and acidity in community supplies. The result usually is water that is acceptable with respect to acidity and hardness, but which has a definite measure of corrosiveness.

To combat the corrosive action of water on the inside of a hot-water tank, several methods may be used. The interior of the tank may be lined with glass or copper, or a magnesium rod may be installed down through the middle of the tank. In the latter, the magnesium bears the brunt of the corrosive action of the water, rather than the zinc-lined tank. Some water tanks in excessively water-corrosive areas are lined with a cement compound. Still another method is to install a "brick" of a chemical compound called MLC-7, which is attached to the interior of the tank near the water inlet.

HOT-WATER REQUIREMENTS

Table 10-1 will give an indication of the average consumption of hot water in different size families. These averages may be altered by the habits of the family, the geographical location and the methods of washing clothes and dishes. A tub bath requires about 7 or 8 gallons of hot water, and a quick shower may consume only 2 or 3 gallons. A dishwasher uses approximately 9 gallons of hot water, whereas washing dishes by hand requires 2 to 7 gallons.

Table 10-1. Average Monthly Hot Water Requirements

A Family of	Consumes, per month
2	700 gallons
3	950 gallons
4	1200 gallons
5	1450 gallons
6	1700 gallons
7	1950 gallons etc.

To arrive at the size of tank required, divide the best "guesstimate" of total gallons consumed monthly by 30 to get daily consumption. Thus, in a family of four, we divide 30 into 1,200, arriving at a recommended size of 40 gallons capacity. However a larger capacity heater is recommended.

Capacity, however, is not the whole story—"Recovery rate" is also a factor. Recovery rate refers to the ability of the water heater to replace depleted supplies of hot water. To calculate this, the following facts should be considered.

One kilowatt hour (1000 watts of electrical power applied to a heating element for one hour) will raise the temperature of 4 gallons of water 100°F. A minimum recovery rate would be the ability to heat a tankful of 50°F water to 150°F in an 8-hour period so that the tank can completely recover overnight and the family will start the day with a new tankful of hot water. Thus, a 40-gallon tank would theoretically require about 10 kilowatt hours for complete recovery, or a single heating unit rated at 1250 watts operating for 8 hours.

In practice, however, most water heaters have a much faster recovery rate. Water heaters with a truly fast recovery rate employ about 9000 watts, making a complete recovery in about 2 hours. Other water heaters may be slower, employing fewer watts, depending on the need of the family.

Wasted Water

Perhaps the most common form of water waste is a drip. A rather slow drip of about one drop each second results in a waste of approximately 200 gallons (or five tankfuls of a 40-gallon tank) per month. A more serious leak which first emerges from the faucet as a smooth stream 3 inches long before it breaks up into drops results in a waste of over 1000 gallons per month, or nearly all the normal hot water consumption of a family of four!

The amount of water standing in a pipe is also related to waste. Information useful in determining the amount of water in a length of pipe is shown in Table 10-2. From these figures, we see that the location of the water heater is of prime importance, for every time you turn on a hot water faucet, you first get cool water which had once been heated by the water heater at some expense.

Modern homes are designed so that the logical location of the furnace and hot water heater from an architectural point

Table 10-2. Standing Water in 12 Feet of Pipe

Pipe Size	Contents
½ inch copper tubing	1 pint (approx.)
⅜ inch copper tubing	.75 pint (approx.)
¼ inch copper tubing	.5 pint (approx.)
¾ inch iron pipe	2.5 pints (approx.)

of view is also best as to its central location with respect to the hot-water faucets. In older homes, however, this criterion was not held to be critical, because hot water was produced as a by-product in the main furnace by means of a water jacket introduced into the coal or oil flame. Many installers still blindly locate the water heater next to the furnace as in older homes, simply because it's the traditional place for it, regardless of the number of pipe feet (and wasted hot water) required to reach each hot-water faucet. The number of running feet of pipe is so critical a factor in hot water economy that many modern electrical water heaters are designed for closet installation, permitting their location right in the kitchen. This is done as much to save water as it is to save space.

GAS WATER HEATERS

Since the characteristics of a gas water heater, including the burner and thermocouple automatic pilot, are similar to those of a gas dryer, most of the operational details are contained in Chapter 4. The only difference between a gas water-heater system and a gas dryer system is the water-heater thermostat, which takes its readings from the interior of the tank.

ELECTRIC WATER HEATERS

There are two main methods of heating water electrically in a water heater. The first method (Fig. 10-1) is called the induction method, wherein electrical heating elements are strapped around the outside of the tank and covered with insulation. The heat from the elements is directed inward (having no other place to go) and passes through the walls of the tank and into the body of the water.

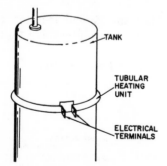

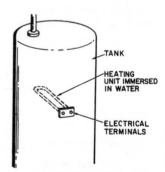

Fig. 10-1. Induction method of heating water electrically.

Fig. 10-2. Immersion method of heating water.

In the other method (Fig. 10-2), called the immersion method, heating elements are passed through the walls of the tank and directly into the water. The point of entry of the tubular unit is made watertight by means of a flange and gasket, and the units themselves are watertight and insulated.

Fig. 10-3 shows the several combinations of units possible in electric water heaters. The tubular units may vary in wattage from 1000 to 2250 watts each. The number of units is directly related to the recovery speed of the appliance.

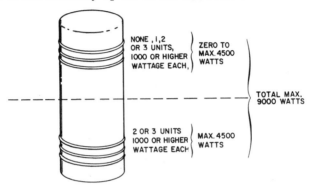

Fig. 10-3. Possible heating-element combinations.

Functioning

Cold water enters the tank through the bottom and leaves the tank at the top, consistent with the principle that warm water rises. Water heaters having a top and bottom heating element consisting of one or more tubular units each are controlled by two thermostats, or a single thermostat having a double-throw action.

Fig. 10-4 explains the functioning of the two thermostats. Starting with a cold tankful of water, the upper heating element only is energized by the upper thermostat. About one quarter of the total volume of water in the tank is heated by the upper elements. The lower elements will not come on until

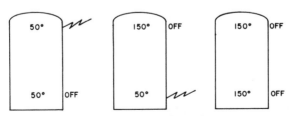

Fig. 10-4. Cycling of upper and lower thermostats.

the upper thermostat has been satisfied. The water heated by the upper element remains at the top of the tank, ready for use.

When the upper thermostat is satisfied, current is then directed by it to the lower thermostat, which now closes a circuit to the lower heating elements. All the remainder of the water in the tank is heated by the lower elements. If, in the meantime, some of the hot water is drawn off, the cold water entering at

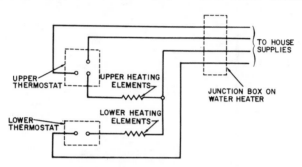

Fig. 10-5. Wiring diagram of typical electrical system.

the bottom of the tank to replace it is heated by the lower heating element. In normal operation, unless the tank is more than three-quarters depleted at any one time, the lower heating element alone is energized, working to heat the water at the bottom of the tank. In practice, the upper heating element is on only about 25% of the time. The wiring diagram (Fig. 10-5) shows a typical layout for an electric water heater employing an upper and lower heating element.

Power Requirements

Electric water heaters require 230 volts, more or less, for efficient operation. If supplied with 115-volt current, they will produce hot water less than half as fast as with full voltage. Some water heaters are rated at 236 or 240 volts, yet local supplies may be only 208 volts. In order to achieve the recovery rate required by demand, a water heater of higher wattage rating than normal is required. Add about 30% to the wattages indicated by the formula: 1,000 watts will raise the temperature of four gallons of water 100°F in one hour—the higher wattage, of course, lowers the recovery time.

Thermostat

The thermostat normally used in an electric water heater is of the bimetallic type (Fig. 10-6), containing a set of contact

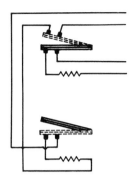

Fig. 10-6. Bimetallic electric water-
heater thermostats.

points which open and close as the bimetallic strip is bent into
a greater or lesser degree of curve under the influence of heat.
This thermostat is similar to the thermostat described in
Chapter 5 dealing with electric range surface-unit thermostats,
except that instead of being influenced by the heat generated
by an electric current passing through it, it responds to the
heat of the water in which the thermostat is immersed. Thus,
it does not cycle on and off at frequent intervals, as does the
range thermostat, but will remain on until the heat of the
water reaches a predetermined high, when it interrupts the
circuit to the heating unit. Note that current flows through
only the very tip of the bimetallic strip.

The water heater thermostat, like other thermostats, has a
temperature range. In the lower unit of a double-unit heater,
the range is from 8° to 15°. In the upper unit the range is
greater—from 20° to 30°. The effect of the difference in ranges
is to work the lower heating unit more frequently than the
upper unit. This means that the upper unit will not come on
until a major portion of the hot water in the tank is depleted.
Changing the setting on the thermostat dial causes the bimetallic strip to travel a longer distance before it can open the
electrical contacts, thus leaving the heating unit on for a longer
time before the thermostat is satisfied.

Pressure-Relief Valve

In order to guard against dangerous pressure build-up in
the event of a failure of the heat control, a pressure-relief
valve (Fig. 10-7) is installed in the cold water line just preceding its entry into the tank. No other valve is permitted between the pressure relief valve and the body of the tank, and
installation should be in a location not exposed to freezing
temperatures. Pressure-relief valves are set to relieve pressure
(by allowing the escape of water) from 25 to 35 psi above

normal water pressure, to a maximum allowable setting of about 125 psi.

Thermal-Limit Switch

In addition to the pressure-relief valve, a further safeguard is obtained by the installation of a thermal high-limit switch. This works in the same manner as the overload protector of an electric motor, except that it is actuated by the heat of the tank wall or the water itself, rather than by an electric current passing through the thermal disc. Thermal-limit switches are set at the factory at a high-limit cutoff setting of about 195°F. They are positioned in series with the heater wiring so as to cut off all power to the heater when the upper limit is reached.

As further protection for the user, a temperature-relief valve is sometimes installed in the hot water line. This is used not so much to protect the tank against dangerous pressure as it is to protect the user from scalding. One such valve features a fusible plug which melts at a predetermined high water temperature, permitting steam and water to escape from the line. The water must then be shut off manually. In an adaptation of this method, a bellows is used which will recover and shut off the water flow when its low temperature setting is satisfied.

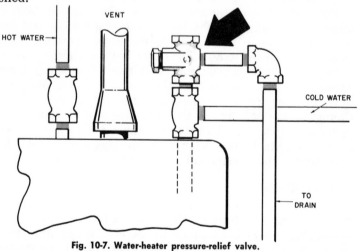

Fig. 10-7. Water-heater pressure-relief valve.

INSTALLATION

As mentioned before, the location of the water heater should be as nearly central as possible with respect to the network of hot-water lines and faucets. Since the kitchen sink leads all other faucets with respect to the number of withdrawals in a given period the preference is to locate the tank as close to the sink as possible.

With respect to piping, the following considerations should be met: never run piping through a cold basement or garage— or excessive heat loss will result. Pipes should never be exposed to freezing temperatures. The diameter of the pipe should be as small as possible, consistent with acceptable flow rates. The smaller the diameter, the less hot water will remain in the pipe, dissipating its heat between withdrawals.

Most electric water heaters are approved for closet installation, which means that they may be installed under the sink counter if desired. Bear in mind in this type of installation, however, that the occasion may arise when the tank must be drained for service. The drain should be easily accessible, and permit the running of a hose to the outdoors for a gravity drain.

Electric water heaters provide a terminal junction box for electrical connections. In the case of high-wattage, fast recovery water heaters, a separately fused branch circuit is required for each heating element. Since electrical connections may differ for each make and model of electric water heaters, it is necessary to consult the manufacturer's literature for specific details of electrical installation. Normally, however, electric water heaters are directly wired to the house distribution box, with an occasional requirement for an On-Off switch mounted in the line before it reaches the appliance.

Fusing should be of the cartridge or circuit-breaker type. The size depends on the wattage of the branch line, according to the following formula:

$$\text{Amperes} = \frac{\text{wattage}}{\text{voltage}}$$

The size of fuse next higher than the amperage found in the formula should be used.

PERFORMANCE CHECKS

Since only two components of an electric water heater can cause electrical failure, it is necessary only to check the continuity of the thermostats and heating units, and the wires of the appliance, in making a performance check. In so doing, do not fail to open the circuit first by removing all fuses, or by actuating the circuit breaker button to Off.

Check the continuity of the thermostat by following the procedure outlined in Chapter 1. In addition, it is necessary to cause the thermostat to cycle On by applying heat to the thermostat housing. This is done by touching it with the tip of a soldering iron, or by directing a heat lamp on it.

The continuity of the heating coils is checked by disconnecting the wires to the terminals and touching them with the probe of the test lamp. No current between the terminals indicates that the unit should be replaced.

Check also for proper grounding by reconnecting all wires (not fuses) to the terminals. Check for continuity between the component terminal and ground. Reverse the leads and check again. An open reading means that the appliance is properly grounded. A closed circuit indicates a shorted condition. Remove the wiring harness and check each component separately, then each segment of wire until the short is isolated.

TROUBLESHOOTING GUIDE

The following common causes and remedies apply to the most frequently reported failures.

No hot water—Check fuses and upper thermostat. The trouble may be a defective high-limit switch or cutoff switch.

Insufficient hot water—All the same checks as for no hot water, plus the lower thermostat and tubular heating units. Also check for loose connections.

Leaks—Check pressure-relief valve or high-limit temperature valve for earlier cycling. New installations may also show evidence of water leaks, but these are usually moisture which has collected in the insulation and condenses when the unit is first turned on.

ELECTRIC MOTORS USED IN HOME APPLIANCES

The most common electric motors used in major appliances as the primary source of power are:

1. Split-phase induction motor.
2. Capacitor-start induction motor.
3. Permanent split-capacitor (PSC) motor.

An induction motor may be described as a motor having: a stationary field, called the stator, through which an electric current flows; and a rotor, fitted within the stator, but not touching it at any point. No electrical connections are made to the rotor. A magnetic field set up by current flowing through the stator coils is induced in the rotor, causing it to revolve at a constant speed.

Motors used in appliances for secondary functions, such as in pumps and fans, may be of the shaded-pole type. This is a low-output, low-speed motor with a relatively low starting power or torque. It has the advantage of design simplicity, well suited to a simple On-Off function. A shaded-pole motor ranges in horsepower from 1/300 to 1/30 hp.

In certain special applications, a universal-type motor is used as the primary source of power. A universal motor may be run on either AC or DC.

Other desirable characteristics of motors for some applications are (1) two-speed operation and (2) reversibility. Washers having "gentle" and "normal" speeds employ two-speed motors. Certain models of dishwashers employ reversible motors, rotation in one direction actuating the impeller, and in the opposite direction actuating the drain pump. These motors will be examined in detail later in this chapter.

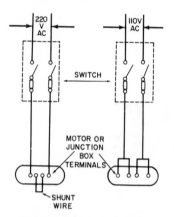

Fig. 11-1. Connections for 110- or 220-volt operation.

It is necessary to design some motors, as in electric dryers so that they may be operated on either 110 or 220 volts. In these appliances, the terminal junction box of the dryer is equipped with a shunt which may be positioned in one of two ways to provide a choice of voltage (Fig. 11-1 illustrates the connections).

SPLIT-PHASE MOTORS

Single-phase electricity of the type commonly found in homes, cannot by itself cause a motor to start rotating, because the magnetic field set up by single-phase current is stationary, and once aligned with this field, the rotor locks in the static position. Once the rotor can be induced to turn, however, its momentum is fed by the pulsing cycles of the current. The problem, then, is to provide a momentary boost to the motor so the rotor will begin to turn.

A split-phase motor (Fig. 11-2) has two windings, a start winding and a run winding. The start winding is composed of many turns of thin wire, setting up a high resistance. The run winding is composed of fewer turns of a heavy wire. The result is a "phase difference."

This phase difference between the start and run windings, both in the circuit momentarily, sets up magnetic forces of unequal strength and direction at different points around the circumference of the stator, causing the rotor to turn, no matter in what position it may have come to rest, in an effort to align itself with the unequal magnetic force. The slight movement then brings the rotor under the influence of a new

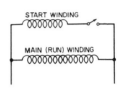

Fig. 11-2. Split-phase motor
wiring diagram.

magnetic direction, causing still more movement. The rapidly changing direction and strength of the rotating magnetic field cause the rotor to pick up speed and momentum.

Once the rotor has achieved run speed, a mechanical or electrical relay opens the circuit to the start winding and the run winding alone is energized. The run winding is sufficiently powerful to keep the motor operating at run speed.

CAPACITOR-START, INDUCTION-RUN MOTORS

In a capacitor-start, induction-run motor (Fig. 11-3) the phase difference of two windings is still used at the start. However, the starting torque is increased by means of an electrolytic start capacitor.

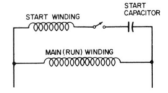

Fig. 11-3. Capacitor-start, induction-run
motor wiring diagram.

CAPACITOR-START, CAPACITOR-RUN MOTORS

In this type of motor (Fig. 11-4) an additional capacitor, called the run capacitor, is permitted to remain in the circuit even after the motor has started. The run capacitor increases the power of the motor.

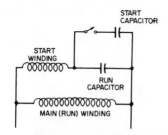

START
CAPACITOR

START
WINDING

RUN
CAPACITOR

MAIN (RUN) WINDING

Fig. 11-4. Capacitor-start, capacitor-run
motor wiring diagram.

PERMANENT SPLIT-CAPACITOR (PSC) MOTOR

The PSC motor (Fig. 11-5) has no start capacitors and relays, making it desirable from the point of view of economy; however, it has low starting torque (power), which limits its application. Briefly, the difference between a PSC motor and an ordinary split-phase motor is that the phase difference is permanent in the former; the run capacitor and auxiliary winding are never disconnected.

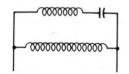

Fig. 11-5. Permanent split-capacitor
PSC motor wiring diagram.

Because of its low starting torque, it can only be used in applications where the initial load is not great. This means that it may be used to power compressors whose head pressure is relieved during cycle-off periods, such as in air conditioners. This is the reason behind the delay recommended in some air conditioners between stopping and starting. Starting the compressor immediately after a stop forces the motor to attempt to start under a full load, which it was never designed to do—damage may result.

SHADED-POLE MOTORS

As mentioned previously, a shaded-pole motor (Fig. 11-6) is used in low-power applications, such as fans and pumps. A portion of each pole is short-circuited by means of a copper strap. These *shaded* portions of the poles are opposed to each other on opposite sides of the axis of each pole. This sets up a phase difference that is sufficient to cause the rotor to turn. The advantages of economy and reliability of the shaded-pole motor are offset by inefficiency, low starting torque, and low output.

222

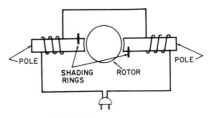

Fig. 11-6. Shaded-pole motor
wiring diagram.

POLE   SHADING   ROTOR   POLE
        RINGS

TWO-SPEED MOTORS

Speed selection in induction-type motors is achieved through the use of two run windings, in addition to the start winding. An electrical switch sends current through only one of these windings for high speed, or connects both of them in parallel for low speed. This is similar to the heat-selector switch discussed in the chapter on electric-range heating units.

REVERSIBLE MOTORS

By crossing the leads to an electric motor, polarity is reversed and the rotor turns in the opposite direction. Crossing the wires is accomplished by a switch, which is sometimes operated by a solenoid energized by the timer.

MOTOR COMPONENTS

Relays—The relay on a motor functions to open the start winding or interrupt the start capacitor circuit once the motor has achieved run speed, normally after about 3 seconds. There are two types of relays: voltage operated and current operated.

The voltage type (Fig. 11-7) is used on the capacitor-start motors only. Its contacts are normally closed so that in the first few seconds at the start, the relay, and hence, the start capacitor are in the circuit. As the motor picks up speed, a current induced in the relay energizes a coil. At about 85% of motor speed, the current is strong enough to overcome the normally closed relay contacts, and the circuit to the start capacitor opens. Note that the start winding stays in the circuit, even after the relay is energized, in the example shown in the drawing.

In the current-type relay (Fig. 11-8) the contacts are normally open. The instantaneous surge of starting current (amperage) actuates an armature, which closes the start winding circuit, and the motor starts. When the motor reaches its normal run speed (after about 3 seconds), the current

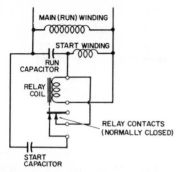

Fig. 11-7. Voltage-type relay.

drops to normal. The weight of the armature now overcomes the force of the coil, and the start winding (or start capacitor, if one is used) is disconnected from the circuit. Current relays may be used without start capacitors, hence are ideal for split-phase motors.

Start capacitor—The start capacitor (Fig. 11-9) increases the initial power of the start winding of an induction motor without increasing the amount of current used. Thus, an extra surge of power is provided to overcome the inertia of the motor and any connected mechanical trains, but without the annoyance of having lights flicker or grow dim as current is drained from them in favor of the appliance. Capacitors are rated in microfarads. Since start capacitors are always teamed up with a relay, the two are usually carefully matched. It is a good idea, when replacing either of these components, to replace the other at the same time, to ensure compatibility.

Run capacitor—A run capacitor (Fig. 11-10) has a similar function to the start capacitor—increasing the power of the electrical supply to the run winding. The run capacitor is not disconnected by the relay, but remains in the circuit even after run speed is achieved.

Motor overload—The overload protector (Fig. 11-11) guards the motor against fluctuations of load or line voltage. If the head pressure of a refrigerator or air conditioner, for example, suddenly increases, the resultant surge of current might be so

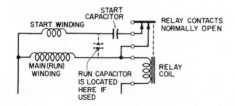

Fig. 11-8. Current-type relay.

224

Fig. 11-9. Start capacitor.

Fig. 11-10. Run capacitor.

great that it would burn out the motor. House voltage which is too low could prevent the rotor from turning; the resultant current drain could burn out the motor. The overload protects the motor in both instances by disconnecting it from the circuit.

At the heart of the overload protector is a small parabolically curved disc made from two metals with different heat coefficients, and bonded together. When an unusual amount of heat is applied to the disc, as in a current increase, the difference in the rate of expansion of the two metals causes the disc to snap into a curve opposite its normal one. This opens the circuit for as long as the heat condition persists. When the temperature returns to normal, the disc snaps back into its original shape, again closing the circuit and permitting normal operation to resume.

Fig. 11-11. Overload protector.

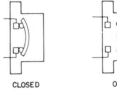

CLOSED   OPEN

PERFORMANCE CHECKS

There is not much that can happen to an electric motor itself; most motor failures are caused by defective auxiliary components, such as relays and capacitors, rather than by defects in the rotor or stator. Replacement of the defective component is normally a simple task, since most such components are mounted outside the motor housing.

225

If a burnout occurs, of course, the entire stator and rotor must either be replaced or rewound. There are shops that specialize in rewinding rotors and, more recently, shops that also take on the more difficult task of rewinding stators. In normal practice, an exchange is made on a one-for-one basis, plus the cost of rebuilding.

In checking the performance of a motor, first make sure that the line voltage and frequency are the same as those listed on the motor or appliance nameplate. If the motor is of the type that can operate on either 110 or 220 volts, make sure the leads are connected properly as indicated at the appliance terminal box.

Run the motor momentarily without load to check start and direction of rotation. Leads are sometimes crossed in reassembly, which causes the motor to change direction. Check by the sound of the motor whether or not the start winding is properly dropping out of the circuit within 2 or 3 seconds after start.

Check branch line fuses to be certain that the amperage rating of the fuse is at least 20% higher than the amperage rating of the motor.

Inspect all bearing surfaces on the motor for signs of lack of lubrication. By the same token, try turning belts, gear trains, and other mechanisms by hand to uncover any signs of mechanical binding.

Check wiring connections to insure that wiring is according to the wiring diagram sometimes provided on the appliance itself. Check for adequate grounding, particularly with rubber-mounted motors. Look for a grounding wire sometimes hidden in one of the rubber feet on the base. Make a clean connection by scraping off any dirt or grease at the terminal connections. Check base and mounting for loose or insecure fastenings. Check any reset buttons with which the motor overload may be equipped.

If a failure has occurred and the motor is suspected, disconnect the wiring harness from the motor and test across the terminals; be sure that the motor overload is not in the open position. If the test lamp glows, the trouble is not in the motor. If an open test results, check each component, such as relays, capacitors, etc., in turn, making the tests described in Chapter 1. Remember when replacing start capacitors to replace the relay as well.

CHAPTER 12

APPLIANCE
FINISHES

For years the traditional appliance finish used by manufacturers has been porcelain enamel that has been baked over a sheet steel base. While it is brittle and may fracture under a severe blow, porcelain is beautiful, easy to clean, stain resistant, and of high structural strength. In recent years, due to the need to shave manufacturing costs, porcelain is no longer found in such widespread use. Few refrigerators, for example, employ porcelain enamel, except in the "top of the line" models, which may offer porcelain enamel interiors. Porcelain is used in the fabrication of dryer and washer baskets and dishwasher tubs.

Improvements in synthetic enamels in recent years have resulted in paint finishes of such durability and attractiveness that they are used almost exclusively for appliance exteriors. Solid color plastics have gained great favor for refrigerator liners, especially because they are compatible with plastic foam insulating processes.

The following is a listing of the appliance finishes in general use, and an outline of the maintenance and care recommended for each.

PORCELAIN ENAMEL

A porcelain enamel finish is made by dipping sheet steel in various dips, consisting of base coatings, acid baths, and two or more spray coatings of a glass-like finish porcelain "slip." This is followed by a baking or firing process. It is an exacting method and the slightest imperfection could be cause for later defects, resulting in a high rate of rejections. Recently, a one-coat process (Fig. 12-1) has been developed which promises to be relatively free from possible imperfections, leading to more widespread use of the finish.

Porcelain is similar to glass in the limitations of stress and strain to which it may be subjected. While it is relatively impervious to scratching, it normally does not require abrasive action to get it clean. Manufacturers caution the user not to

(Courtesy Appliance Manufacturer)

Fig. 12-1. Spraying of porcelain "slip".

attempt to clean the finish while it is hot, as in a kitchen range, because temperature stresses may cause "crazing" (Fig. 12-2), a finish defect characterized by criss-cross lines in an arrangement suggesting parchment.

Porcelain is stain resistant, but not necessarily stain proof. Acids such as those in lemon juice will attack the finish if they are allowed to remain on the surface too long.

Defects in manufacture will result in *tension chips, fish scale,* or *curling.* The first is characterized by long, parallel

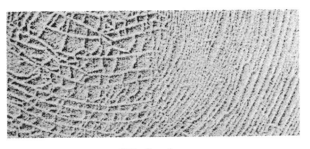

(A) Fracture.

(B) Crazing.

(C) Tension chip.

Fig. 12-2. Common defects in porcelain enamel finishes.

cracks in the porcelain surface, usually along seam lines. Fish scale resembles widely scattered half-moon dents or cracks, which sometimes delay their appearance for days or weeks after manufacture. Curling refers to the sharp ridges formed at the edges of the enameled panel. These are sometimes hidden by trim and therefore are of no concern. However, when they are visible under normal use of the product, they will be considered cause for rejection.

Fractures of the enamel coating are almost always the result of an accidental blow by a sharp, heavy instrument. A typical porcelain fracture looks like the weather maps during a hurricane, with an "eye" at the center, surrounded by concentric crack rings. Fractures and other serious defects in porcelain enamel normally cannot be repaired economically, and the entire panel should be replaced.

BAKED-ON ENAMEL PAINT

The *synthetic* enamels are popular for several reasons; they not only provide a high-gloss, attractive finish, but they are nearly as durable and stain resistant as porcelain enamel. Structural members and panels facing the exterior of the appliance may be finish-coated the same as genuine porcelain exteriors. In addition, an enamel paint can be refinished in the event of damage, using a spray can with color-matched enamel. In most respects, the enamel paint used for appliances is the same as that used for automobiles.

The new synthetics rarely, if ever, require any maintenance beyond an occasional wipe with a damp cloth. For more stubborn stains, rub the surface gently with a solution of mild bar soap and water, or a high-grade wax cleaner. Abrasives should never be used on an enamel paint surface. A wax finish coat normally is not needed, as the enamel will keep a bright, gleaming surface indefinitely if it is not abused.

Another reason for the popularity of enamel paint finishes is the opportunity they afford to color match all the appliances in the kitchen. If a new refrigerator in color is added to the kitchen, the existing appliances may be sprayed with enamel to match the color of the refrigerator exactly.

Spray Painting

Spraying enamel on a panel surface requires a minimum amount of care and preparation. It can usually be done right in the user's home if only a few minor scratches are to be repaired. Complete directions are usually provided on the spray can, but the cardinal points in paint spraying are worthy of mention.

Be sure to ventilate the room adequately. The surface to be sprayed should be cleaned thoroughly with soap and water, being careful to rinse away any residual soap film. Now wipe dry with a clean cloth. Mask any areas not to be painted with masking tape, being careful not to get fingermarks on the panel. "Roughing up" the surface may or may not be required.

When applying the enamel, be careful to hold the spray can the correct distance away from the panel surface, normally indicated by the paint manufacturer. Spraying should be done with a sweeping left to right motion. Start the spray while still off the panel and release the spray button after you have passed the trailing edge. Keep the spray cone in motion, never letting it dwell in one spot. If one pass over the surface does not cover the defect or the old finish, wait for the first pass to dry, then make another pass, repeating the process until the panel is covered satisfactorily. A few practice passes on a sheet of metal will tell you how fast or slow the passes should be to avoid puddling.

SOLID-COLOR PLASTICS

Plastic finishes are used in appliances wherever no great amount of structural strength or heat-resistance is required. Plastic finishes should be cleaned with warm water and soap. Never use any kind of abrasives or wax cleaners on plastic surfaces.

Some components, such as water-pump housings and front panels on air conditioners are sometimes made of high heat-resistant plastics, such as propropylene, which is also resistant to detergent, bleach, and alkalis, as well as the action of sand and grit which would ordinarily be corrosive to metal.

Control panels, escutcheons, trim, and similar appliance components are normally made of plated metals or anodized aluminum, which require very little care beyond an occasional wipe with a damp cloth.

RUST STAINS

To remove rust stains from the interiors of dishwashers, and washer and dryer tubs and baskets, add ½ teaspoon of oxalic acid crystals, obtainable at a drug store, and let the appliance run through a cycle, followed by a wash with regular detergent. WARNING—*oxalic acid is a poison, and should be handled with great care.*

INDEX